The Spiritual
Physics of Light

The Spiritual Physics of Light

How We See, Feel, and Know Truth

Aaron D. Franklin

Published by the Religious Studies Center, Brigham Young University, Provo, Utah, in cooperation with Deseret Book Company, Salt Lake City, Utah.
Visit us at rsc.byu.edu.

Printed in the United States of America by Sheridan Books, Inc.

DESERET BOOK is a registered trademark of Deseret Book Company.
Visit us at DeseretBook.com.

For color versions of the figures, see spiritualphysicsoflight.com.
Cover and interior design by Emily V. Strong.

ISBN 978-1-9503-0407-3

Library of Congress Cataloging-in-Publication Data

Names: Franklin, Aaron (Professor of Electrical Engineering), author.
Title: The spiritual physics of light : how we see, feel, and know truth / Aaron D. Franklin.
Description: Provo : Religious Studies Center, Brigham Young University, [2021] | Includes index. | Summary: "This book explores the connections between what scientists know about light empirically and what members of The Church of Jesus Christ of Latter-day Saints have learned about light doctrinally. Each chapter contains discussions on how we see, feel, and know truth (which is light) by relating and connecting physical principles of electromagnetic radiation to gospel truths about light"-- Provided by publisher.
Identifiers: LCCN 2020047316 | ISBN 9781950304073 (hardback)
Subjects: LCSH: Light--Religious aspects--Church of Jesus Christ of Latter-day Saints. | Light--Religious aspects--Mormon Church. | Light. | Jesus Christ--Influence. | Knowledge, Theory of.
Classification: LCC BX8643.L58 F73 2021 | DDC 248--dc23
LC record available at https://lccn.loc.gov/2020047316

To those who have been

"a lamp unto my feet

and a light unto my path"

(Psalm 119:105)

Contents

Preface

For as long as I can remember, I have wanted to be an electrical engineer. My interest began early on when individuals from Motorola visited my elementary school and, while dressed in garb that looked like space suits, talked about how they made electronics. It sounded exciting and impressive, and I wanted to be a part of something like that. My interest deepened as I grew more fascinated by the invisible force of electricity and all it can accomplish.

As I continued through school, my fascination grew beyond electricity, and I developed a passion for exploring materials and forces in the universe that cannot be fully understood with just our physical senses. For instance, I knew when I flipped a switch, electricity would *flow* through a wire and cause something electronic to be powered—but how? I knew the opposite poles of magnets presented a substantial *attractive* force—but why? I knew that *something* made it possible for a radio to pick up a music station broadcast from many miles away and turn the invisible signal into sound—but what? These questions swirled in my mind throughout my youth.

Among all of these seemingly intangible forces, my interest in the nature of light deepened, specifically around 2001 while I was taking a college physics course and concurrently teaching an early morning seminary class. The course of study that year in seminary was Doctrine and Covenants, and the juxtaposition of investigating the physical properties of light in my physics course while pondering the doctrinal aspects of light found in Doctrine and Covenants 50, 88, and 93 became the perfect confluence. I found myself focusing a great deal of my gospel studies on the connection between what we know about light scientifically and the role that light plays spiritually.

In the years that followed, I further incorporated the doctrines of light into the lessons I taught at Church, the talks I gave, and my personal study. I often found myself longing for further commentary from gospel scholars on the topic of light and its spiritual implications. At one point, while expressing these feelings to my wife, she said, "Well, it sounds like you're going to need to write that book yourself!" That was more than eight years ago. The encouragement from my wife was great in principle but not exactly simple to execute amid the steady onslaught of a busy life with a young family, Church responsibilities, and a demanding job. Besides, it was admittedly difficult for me to conclude that I was the best person to take on such a task.

At length, with the encouragement of other close friends, I decided to start collecting and organizing years of accumulated notes to see how they might all come together if I were to write a book. Around this time, I made a phone call to one of the people in my life whom I always turn to for advice and counsel: my mission president, Richard Jones. I asked President Jones whether he thought a book focused on the connections between the physical and spiritual aspects of light would be interesting and whether he would be willing to give me feedback on a draft should I get it all put together. His enthusiastic "Yes!" was the final gust of wind I needed to sail on toward completing this book.

President Jones shared with me that a family friend of his, a tremendous gospel scholar who had produced a number of renowned works during his fruitful career, gave memorable advice near the end of his life. When asked what he considered to be his most significant gospel study, this prolific scholar answered that the most important study is the one he never did. He explained that were he able to live his life over again, he would abandon many of the topics for which he had become a leading scholar and *dedicate his life to the study and understanding of light*. After sharing this with me, President Jones said he couldn't pass up the chance to read whatever I put together on the topic. To be honest, I so respect and love him that if this book is destined to have a lifetime readership of only a handful of people and one of them is him, then it will have all been worth it.

To the reader who may have far greater experience studying light than myself, I hope you will forgive the absence of any vital information or considerations. What is intended herein is most certainly not comprehensive, nor is it meant to be academically exhaustive. The purpose of this book is to provide spiritual edification. Much of what is presented is my own personal perspective or interpretation by which I make connections between the spiritual aspects of light and scientific data that is measurable by the temporal world. However, the instrument most important for measurement during study of the content herein is the Spirit. In my experience, the Holy Ghost can speak to spirits that are truly interested in edification through the study of light.

For those who have happened upon this book out of curiosity, perhaps with some trepidation or timidity owing to the title and scientific content, please know that the intended readership is definitely not limited to those with a science or engineering degree! My goal is to provide some thought-provoking perspectives to us all on the spiritual significance of light. While I do include some core scientific aspects of light to provide depth to the discussion for interested persons, you can certainly dwell less on those aspects and focus on the scriptural discussions of light that may be of greater interest to you.

The intended audience of this book includes members of The Church of Jesus Christ of Latter-day Saints because the discussion and analysis of the spiritual aspects of light are founded upon Latter-day Saint scripture and doctrine. However, it would pain me to suggest that this book is of no interest or value to readers who do not share my faith. I certainly have been instructed and inspired by religious texts and individuals from many other faiths, since light is an important power among virtually all theological perspectives. In like manner, I hope the perspectives, principles, and testimony herein will be of value to readers less familiar with my core beliefs and will perhaps even inspire them to seek further information or understanding concerning them (I recommend starting with www. comeuntochrist.org).

If you've ventured this far into the preface and are still wondering—Why a book on the spiritual physics of light?—keep in mind that light has become an important part of virtually every aspect of the modern world. It not only keeps us warm and gives us vision but is also responsible for our communication technology, the internet, space travel, electrical power generation, and so on. Is the physical light we use in these applications actually related to the spiritual light of the gospel, such as the Light of Christ? Can we apply what we know scientifically about light to the doctrine of light in the gospel of Jesus Christ? These, and many similar questions, have worked on my mind for years and are at the very heart of this book. I do not suggest that all are answered definitively herein; rather, discussion and scriptural connections are provided to stir the minds of readers in hopes that they will continue their own study of this eternal power. I propose that all forms of light have spiritual significance and are influential on every person's soul; hence, a study of light that includes both physical and spiritual attributes is warranted. Whether or not you have been—or have yet to become—inundated with the same depth of wonder regarding light as I have, I hope this book will provide an opportunity for you to see this power in an entirely new . . . light.

For color versions of the figures, see spiritualphysicsoflight.com.

Acknowledgments

This book represents hundreds of conversations filling countless hours over the course of many years. One of my great fears is that I have done a woefully inadequate job of capturing the powerful insights, ideas, and inspirations shared by those from whom I have been blessed to learn. I am deeply grateful to all who have been willing to discuss, read, edit, or otherwise review the content herein—your contributions were vital to the development of this book.

I express my sincere gratitude to Richard W. Jones, Adam De Oliveira, and Jake Smith, all of whom have so generously read multiple versions of the chapters, including early rough drafts. Beyond their patient reading were the long discussions we would have over lunch or on the phone, late at night or early in the morning, while driving or hiking through the woods—wherever and whenever the time could be found. Many others were kind enough to read or provide invaluable feedback on the book and its topics, including Steve Walters (my first reader!), Claudia Walters, Craig and Maria Whitehead, Craig Middledorf, Phil Fairbourn, Jean Jones, and Elizabeth Franklin.

I am also grateful to my children—Ellie, Grant, and Blake—who provide me daily with opportunities to understand how light is radiated and received. Furthermore, it was, in part, time with them that was sacrificed to do the studies herein.

Amid the incredible kindness and contributions of so many, I benefited most significantly from the steady support of my wife, Lianne Franklin. From her considerable editing to make sense out of much of my nonsense, to her encouragement and sacrifice in allowing me to spend so much of my already limited time at home on writing this book—it simply would not have come together without her. What's more, Lianne has been the loving emotional support and patient listening ear that has kept me from abandoning ship at many points along this path to publication.

It has been a privilege to work with the BYU Religious Studies Center (RSC) through the publication process for this book. The detailed evaluation and feedback from the double-blind review process provided me with valuable advice that unquestionably improved the work. I also extend a special thanks to Shirley Ricks and her intern, Meghan Rollins Wilson, for their thoroughness in editing the book and going beyond the colloquial "crossing the *t*'s and dotting the *i*'s," to the point where they made enormously useful and notable contributions. Shirley was also consistently responsive and supportive, even to the whims of an overly excited author with many rudimentary questions. This book never would have seen the light of day without the initial and ongoing support of Scott Esplin, and the quality of the final product would only have been a shadow of its present state without the assistance of Brent Nordgren and Emily V. Strong. In short, the entire BYU RSC team was phenomenal to work with and pivotal in bringing this book about light, to light.

My gratitude also extends to prophets, ancient and modern, who have been as captivated by the subject of light as I am and, above all, to my Heavenly Father and his Beloved Son, Jesus Christ—I have always known they were there. I formally learned of them when I was a young teenager; I discovered their power while serving as a missionary in the beautiful state of Georgia; and I have felt their love for me and all people countless times in my life since. Their love is light, even the Light of Christ, which so many of these pages are dedicated to exploring and understanding.

1

Observations on Light

Standing at the entrance of the tunnel I could see ahead of me a darkness so absolutely black it seemed a solid.[1]

—Jim White, discoverer of Carlsbad Caverns

Our tour guide warned us one last time that if anyone felt uncomfortable and wanted to back out, this was the last chance to do so. After scanning the anxious faces, and satisfied we were all serious about staying, he smiled and said, "Here we go!" With that, we were plunged into complete blackness.

It was the early summer of 2004, and my wife, Lianne, and I were crossing the country on our way to an internship at Purdue University. We were still newlyweds, and, earlier, in our excitement to plan out this road trip from Arizona to the Midwest, we had purchased a map of the United States and hung it in our apartment. After sketching out the most direct route, we identified a few places we wanted to visit and carefully added detours to include them. Lianne remembered visiting Carlsbad Caverns in New Mexico as a young teenager and had been so enthralled by the massive caves that she wanted me to see them as well.

Located at the northern end of the Guadalupe Mountains, Carlsbad Caverns is about one hundred miles from the nearest major city, El Paso, Texas. With nothing but empty desert in between the caverns and El Paso, the mountains provide some relief to the expanse of sagebrush and small cacti. Having grown up in Arizona, I could appreciate the beauties of the desert, but one thing was clear: this was not the type of place one simply happened upon—Carlsbad Caverns is definitely a destination location!

When we got there, I remember being somewhat unimpressed with the entrance to the caves and found myself wondering if this was worth the two-hour detour. Lianne was newly expecting our first child and not feeling her best, so we opted to ride the elevator rather than hike down through more than 750 feet of earth to begin the tour in the so-called Big Room. While exiting the elevator, my initial impressions quickly vanished as I took in the view of an expansive underearth chamber. I soon found myself captivated by the story of Jim White, a boy who had discovered the caverns when he was just fifteen or sixteen years old.

Jim White was born in 1882 and grew up learning the trade of cattle ranching. While out looking for stray cattle some distance from the ranch, he noticed what looked like a plume of dark smoke rising in the distance. He drew closer only to discover that the perceived smoke was actually a thick (and seemingly endless) cloud of bats flying out from a hole in the ground. The right combination of juvenile curiosity and uncommon bravery led Jim to begin solo expeditions down his newly discovered cave. In the ensuing years he would map out miles of caverns, naming most of them, and would lead small tour groups through the cave with little more than some ropes and lanterns.

There were two things I learned from Jim White's story during that trip to Carlsbad Caverns that left a lasting impression on me. The first is that you should *always* have at least three sources of light with you when in a cave—a mantra Jim came to live by. The second was how profound and almost tangible the complete absence of light can be.

When we entered one of the rooms in the innermost depths of the caverns, the tour guide told how Jim had been exploring the caves by himself one day and had been in the very place we were standing. While crossing an area with a collection of stalagmites, Jim tripped and his lantern flew from his hand, crashing in the distance and extinguishing his only source of light. Regarding the intense effect of losing a sole light source in the cave, Jim would later say, "It seemed as though a million tons of black wool descended upon me."[2] The ensuing time spent groping around the cave for his lantern led Jim to develop his maxim that one should never enter a cave without at least three sources of light.

After relating this story, our tour guide explained that he would be turning off the lights and asked if anyone wanted to leave before acquainting us with the same total blackness (and, somewhat eerily, in the same place) that Jim White had experienced more than one hundred years earlier. He explained that many people are disturbed by the experience and encouraged anyone who had reservations about it or struggled with claustrophobia to take the offer to temporarily leave the cavern and go over to a distant, lit corridor. Some members of our small group relented and were escorted out of the area to wait. Satisfied, the guide pressed a button on the wall, and we were plunged into total blackness.

Despite the tour guide's warning that our eyes would never adjust, I could still feel my brain struggling to force my pupils to adapt to the loss of light. Within seconds it became obvious that all my blinking and squinting were futile. For a cave that had looked so large, it now seemed like the entire world had suddenly sucked in around my body as the "tons of black wool" extinguished all the space that had once been there. Physically, the cave felt colder and oppressive. Emotionally, the lack of light made the cave seem so lonely. The tour guide reassured us we were still perfectly safe, but after nearly a full minute, fellow tourists were getting audibly restless and uncomfortable with the situation. There was a click, and instantly the lights came on and reestablished the ample space that had seemed lost to blackness. Sighs of relief echoed around the cavern. We had just experienced a mere sixty seconds of the complete and utter absence of light, otherwise known as darkness.

Have you ever experienced such complete darkness? Have you wondered why it is more unsettling to be plunged into total blackness than it is to close your eyes when lying in a dark room to sleep? Before that

experience in the depths of Carlsbad Caverns, my exposure to darkness never usually lasted more than a few frustrating moments while I allowed my eyes to adjust to a sudden change in illumination by letting my pupils widen in order to take in more light. Concepts that I was previously aware of took on new meanings, such as how darkness cannot be turned on, only light can be switched on or off. It's not that we choose darkness, but rather that we opt to reduce light; hence, darkness is a consequence rather than a direct option. What seems like mere semantics actually has profound implications.

Light affects our lives in far more ways than just enabling sight. The light you can see (that enables you *to* see) is only a tiny fraction of the broad spectrum of light that exists. Light spans from radio waves to gamma rays (and that's just the light we can identify scientifically). Have you ever considered what, if any, connections exist between the physical light that can be scientifically measured (and physiologically detected) and the spiritual light that is referred to throughout the scriptures? To set the stage for some more in-depth discussions regarding the spiritual nature of light—how it is radiated, detected, discerned, and so forth—the most prominent uses or applications of light in our daily lives are briefly introduced below.

Light and Dark

Light and dark—isn't this the age-old dichotomy? Light versus dark has represented everything from good versus evil to inviting versus creepy. Arguably, the most well-known use in popular culture is from the Star Wars stories and films, where the light side versus the dark side of a mysterious power called the "force" is at the heart of each plotline. The compelling contrast—truly, the very definition of contrast—between light and dark inspires good and defines evil in a way that, to me, is clearer and more understandable than any other pairing of opposites.

From the time that most of us are young children, the absence of light is feared. Are you afraid of the dark? Most kids, and even many adults, are. Why is that? Perhaps the most common reason is because of the unknown that could be hiding in the dark—if you can't see what's there, then the imagination can invent all sorts of things to put there. In fact, the unknown nature of what lurks in the dark leads many to seek to hide things they are ashamed of "in the dark," so as to keep others from knowing about them.

When discussing darkness, we are most often referring to the absence of a very specific type of light—the type we can see. Yet, there is far more light than what the optic nerves in our eyes are able to detect. Visible light is only a small portion of what is called "electromagnetic radiation." In subsequent chapters of this book, the implications of the many other types of light, or electromagnetic radiation, will be considered, including what is called "spiritual light."

Light and Heat

It doesn't take a tech geek to appreciate the marvelous invention of an infrared vision system, known in one form as "night vision." As will be discussed in chapter 3, infrared thermography is a way for visualizing light that is outside the spectrum of visible light. It has been scientifically proven that *everything* emits light *at all times*. At least one source for this constant radiation of light is heat. I'm not just referring to how a fire is visible because it is hot, and thus you see the flames. Actually, the light emitted by most things is *not* visible but is still associated with their temperatures. A person with a body temperature of 98.6 degrees Fahrenheit will emit a distinctly different type of light than someone with a temperature of 102 degrees; this discrepancy can be picked up by a simple consumer product called a thermal scan thermometer.

Consider the gospel significance of how *everything*, including every person, radiates a distinct type of light at all times. In chapter 3, the correlation with what I call "spiritual body radiation" will be discussed to reflect how electromagnetic radiation is so much more than just the light that we can see or that is based on body temperature—levels of spiritual light can also have a notable, detectable impact on those around us.

Light and Communication

Another use of light that is of great importance in the modern age relates to various forms of communication. Light has become the ubiquitous medium for transmitting information. This includes everything from internet data carried thousands of miles in fiber optic cables, to cell phone conversations transported from a tiny phone to a nearby tower and ultimately to the desired recipient. While initial telephone communications were carried using electricity, light has become the dominant medium for transmitting our countless forms of communication and data. This type of light is not visible to the human eye (thankfully, as the world would look like quite a mess!) but has a powerful effect on our daily lives.

If as mortals we have managed to figure out how to use light to communicate from long distances, what sort of capabilities does God have with light? If I can press a few buttons on my cell phone and within moments have a live conversation with someone halfway around the world, is it not perfectly reasonable to embrace God's ability to hear our prayerful communications and to readily answer them?

Light and Life

Light has life-giving power. Consider the critical process of photosynthesis in plants that gives us oxygen to breathe. Or consider the process by which the earth has been warmed to a survivable, viable temperature for life. Light provided by the sun makes these processes, and thus life, possible. At a distance of ninety-three million miles from the earth, it is remarkable how much influence light from the sun has! And remember, it's not just visible light that the sun is sending to the earth but light of many different and necessary types. Despite the distance, light from the surface of the sun is able to arrive on earth in just over eight minutes!

It is no coincidence that the Savior, Jesus Christ, is often compared to the sun because of his unmatched influence on our eternal lives. Consider the rapidity of his response to our needs. Consider the crucial role his Atonement plays in our spiritual lives. And consider how there would be no life without him. These parallels between Christ and the sun, and further between Christ and light, will be discussed in the final chapter, "The Light of the World."

Isn't it remarkable how diverse the roles of light are and how they affect our lives? It turns out that Jim White's experience with total blackness in the caves of Carlsbad, New Mexico, was only scratching the surface of all that light does in our lives today. If Jim had truly encountered the total absence of all types of light, he would quickly have frozen to death in addition to temporarily losing his sight. In a similar circumstance, we also would have lost cell phone service (well, not equally important, but still an effect of having no light). These observations on the diverse uses and implications of light will be built upon as we consider the spiritual aspects of light and how they relate to what we know scientifically. The discussions in this book will clarify how this versatile force gives us the ability to see, feel, and know truth, which, after all, is light (see Doctrine and Covenants 84:45).

Notes

1.   Jim L. White, *Jim White's Own Story: The Discovery and History of Carlsbad Caverns* (Chicago: Curt Teich, 1932), 2.

2.   White, *Jim White's Own Story*, 5.

2

Basic Physics of Light

What I am going to tell you about [light] is what we teach our physics students in the third or fourth year of graduate school. . . . It is my task to convince you not to turn away because you don't understand it. You see my physics students don't understand it. . . . That is because I don't understand it. Nobody does.[1]

—Richard P. Feynman, Nobel Laureate

Readers who are intimidated by physics may be thinking, "OK, I'm skipping this chapter because I hate physics/science/math!" First of all, you're not alone. Understanding the physical nature of something as complex as light is no small feat. The quote at the beginning of this chapter is from Dr. Richard Feynman, one of the greatest theoretical physicists of all time. Feynman was gifted at communicating the complex aspects of physics in a way that was more accessible to those without direct training in the discipline. At the same time, Feynman recognized that all of the education and experience in the world would not result in perfect mastery when it came to the physics of light. So, as Feynman asked of his audience decades ago, I ask of you now: Don't turn away because you don't understand.

It is certainly not the purpose of this chapter to make you feel like you're suffering through a physics textbook. Instead, I hope to provide a simplified description of the physical properties of light that can then be considered in relation to spiritual principles while (hopefully) remaining engaging enough to keep your interest! For those desiring finer details, endnotes have been included to provide more insight into some of the topics.

What You Already Know about Light

Let's start with the basics by building on things you already know: when there is light, you are able to see; and when there is no light, you cannot see. If you have ever used a flashlight on a dark night or in a dark room, then you have witnessed a key physical aspect of light: it moves in a certain direction. Light does not necessarily spread from its source in all directions (think of how the beam of a flashlight illuminates things primarily in its path).[2] How then does an entire room become a bit brighter even if a flashlight is only directly lighting up a particular swath of the space? That happens because a portion of the light bounces off most things, causing much of the space outside its original path to also be lit up slightly. Your ability to read this sentence on the page is based on light bouncing off the page and then entering your eye.[3]

Something else you already know about light is that it can heat things. If you step out of the shade of a tree and into the sunshine, you will feel noticeable warmth from the light. This example actually represents light's directionality and heating power. Believe it or not, by realizing these two simple aspects of light—that it moves in a specific direction and that it heats things—you have already delved into some serious quantum mechanics! What befuddled the world's best scientists one hundred years ago about light was how something *intangible* could move in a specific direction (even though it is a wave), and at the same time do something *physically tangible*, such as cause an object of some type to heat up (suggesting that light is a particle). Scientists dubbed this unique behavior of light "wave-particle duality."

Light Is Electromagnetic Radiation

In the scientific world, light is referred to as "electromagnetic radiation." The light we are able to see with our eyes is just a tiny portion of the possible types of electromagnetic radiation; this range (or portion) is called "visible light." What I mean by range is that electromagnetic radiation has certain energies or wavelengths to it (we'll discuss wavelength more in just a moment). Visible light is a certain energy range of electromagnetic radiation. Visible light that is red is of a different energy than light that is blue. In this book, the term *light* will be used to refer to all forms (energies) of electromagnetic radiation, not just the part that is visible.

Now let's break down electromagnetic radiation. First, consider what you know about magnetic fields. Whether you have simply used a magnet to hang something on your refrigerator door or have had an MRI (magnetic resonance imaging) scan, you undoubtedly have some experience with magnetic force. That force (from a magnetic field) is what holds the magnet to your refrigerator and is one of the basic forces of nature. Another such force is that of an electric field. Just as there are two opposite poles on a magnet (north and south), and the like poles (north and north) repel each other while the opposite poles (north and south) attract each other, there are positive electric charges and negative electric charges that are responsible for an electric field (like charges repel, opposites attract). Any time you have a positive charge separated from a negative charge, you have an electric field between those opposite charges that (in a way) represents their compulsion to come together (this is why there are positive and negative symbols on the opposite terminals of a battery).[4]

So, we have a magnetic field that can be felt when permanent magnets are attracted to metal objects, and we have an electric field that can be felt in the form of static electricity when you scuff your feet on carpet and then touch (and shock) someone. It turns out that light is a unique combination of an <u>electric</u> field and a *magnetic* field that is tied together in what we call an <u>electro</u>*magnetic* wave. Why a *wave*?—because light is *always*

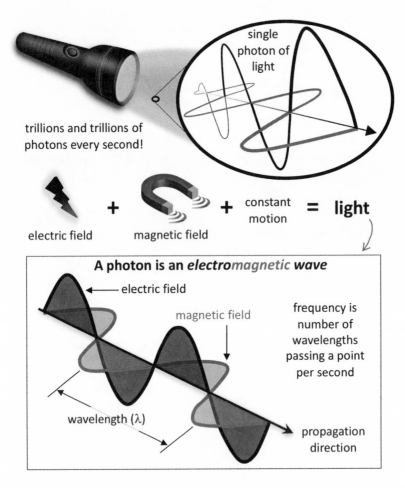

Figure 2.1. Light consists of electromagnetic radiation and comes in units of photons (small, individual pieces of light). A common flashlight emits trillions and trillions of photons every second. Photons are always moving (at about the speed of light) and are made up of a magnetic field and an electric field combined orthogonally. Photons never stop moving unless they are absorbed by something. For color versions of the figures, see spiritualphysicsoflight.com.

moving, a characteristic that is scientifically referred to as "propagating" or "radiating."[5] You cannot store light as you would store electric charge in a battery. Just think: light consists of a combination of two powerful invisible forces! Figure 2.1 gives a breakdown of these concepts leading to the electromagnetic wave (light).

Now that the electromagnetic part is explained, what about the radiation part? The reason that light is referred to as electromagnetic radiation is not exactly based on what we typically think of when we hear the word *radiation*, such as nuclear reactors, bombs, or cancer-causing invisible beams. As mentioned above, the word *radiation* here is referring to the fact that light is always moving (i.e., radiating) with a certain amount of energy; however, once we are talking about how light moves, it is often more intuitive to talk about its wavelength, which is inversely proportional to its energy (i.e., when one goes up the other goes down, and vice versa).[6] Electromagnetic waves (photons of light) can have anything from extremely small to extremely large wavelengths (with corresponding extremely high to extremely low energies), but all of these wavelengths are still considered light.

The Energy of Light

If all energies of light were suddenly visible to the human eye, the world would appear as nothing but a bright blur of frenzied motion. I like to compare that idea to a pyrotechnic laser show happening simultaneously with the finale of a fireworks display, multiplied in intensity by a billion. There is *that* much light constantly passing around you and through you at any given moment. Envision all the ways that you directly use various forms of light throughout your day. Most obvious, of course, is the visible light that allows you to see. There is light from the sun that warms the earth, allows plants to grow, and has the potential to burn your skin. Then there is the light that carries your cell phone conversations across the city, state, country, or even world. Radio or satellite waves of light are picked up by the antennae on your car to allow you to tune in to your favorite music or talk station. Packets of information are carried by light waves to your smartphone or tablet or computer so that you can receive email messages or social networking updates or web page content. More generally, any time information (data, voice, video, and so forth) is sent or received without wires, light is being used as the medium to transmit the

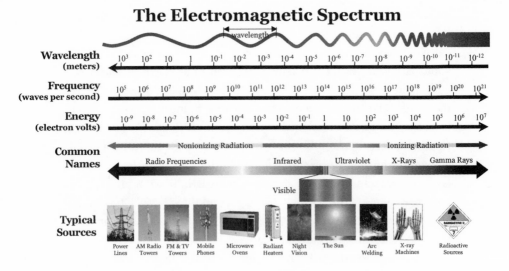

Figure 2.2. Electromagnetic spectrum for all three attributes of light: wavelength, frequency, and energy. Examples of sources of light at various wavelengths are given in the included pictures. Note: light is also referred to as waves. (See spiritual physicsoflight.com.)

information from the sender to the receiver. Needless to say, it's a good thing there is only a specific range of light that is visible to the human eye.

What distinguishes these various types of light that are all around you? Well, besides the information that has been encoded into them (something we will discuss in detail in chapter 5), it is their energies that make them distinct. Let's turn our attention to the electromagnetic spectrum shown in figure 2.2. While it may seem a bit heavy on technical aspects, the spectrum has interesting significance when related to spiritual light. From this electromagnetic spectrum, you can observe that the optic nerve of the human eye is able to detect light composed of energies from approximately 1.8 to 3.1 electron volts, which correspond to wavelengths of 400 to 700 nanometers and a frequency range of 428 to 750 terahertz. For most people, these scientific values hold little meaning—and yet these three interrelated attributes determine nearly all of light's scientifically known behavior.

Let's start with the electron volt (abbreviated eV). This is a measure of energy that you're likely more familiar with than you realize. Think of a standard AA battery, which has a rated voltage of 1.5 volts (V). Voltage is essentially a measure of energy—energy that is either stored or present based on an electric potential difference (i.e., the separation of electric charges of different polarity—positive and negative). Where is the *e* coming from to make it eV? Well, the *e* is a constant of the physical universe with a specific, fixed value or number, just like pi (π). So, eV and V are very similar, modified only by a constant.[7] What happens if a single AA battery of 1.5 volts does not provide sufficient energy to power something? You add more batteries to increase the energy that is provided.[8] The more energy (more batteries), the bigger the workload that can be accomplished. Energy is used to do work. The type of work depends on the energy and how the source of the energy is implemented, which, in the case of the batteries, is determined based on the electrical circuit or gadget they are added to. Light has energy, similar to how batteries have voltage. Thus light accomplishes a great deal of work, from photosynthesis in plants to warming the earth.

The fact that light has energy is what makes it like a particle, or in other words, something tangible. You may be thinking, "Wait a minute, batteries have energy that provides *electricity*, and *that* isn't a particle nor is it tangible." However, electricity is actually quite tangible; it is the flow of electrons, which are one of the smallest known *particles* in the universe. Have you ever been electrocuted? When I was a teenager, one popular pastime for self-inflicted torture was touching the wire of the electric fence in my friend's backyard. One night, a group of us came up with a brilliant, albeit cruel, plan. We formed a line by linking hands, then the boy on one end grabbed the arm of an innocent and unsuspecting sleeper on the couch while the boy on the other end of the line touched the electric fence. Standing in that line, we could all feel the jolt of electricity flowing through our bodies, especially in our wrists. This included the poor, unsuspecting sleeper! Not one of the finer moments of my youth . . . When you are electrocuted, you can actually feel the tiny electron particles flowing through you. Like the electrons that flow to create electricity, light has energy that gives it momentum; thus light is also (in a way) a particle, even though it has no mass.[9]

Frequency and Wavelength of Light

We've established that light has energy, and this makes it behave like a particle. Now let's consider the other aspect of light: that it also behaves like a wave. Imagine for a moment a wave in the ocean—What is it like? For one, it does not stand still; to do so would destroy the wave. Other observations show that the wave has a certain size and that there is some time between one wave and the next, so each wave is discrete. All of these aspects of an ocean wave are true of light waves as well. Perhaps most important of all, waves cannot be stored, no matter if they are made of light, ocean water, or anything else. Waves must be generated from some source.

Regarding the movement of light waves, the analogy to ocean waves becomes a bit less relevant. A better comparison, though, it is not necessarily the same physical process, would be to think about how a ribbon eel swims in water.[10] The eel moves in what would be called a "wavelike pattern" at a certain *frequency* and *wavelength*. So where did those two terms come from? Look back at figure 2.1, where the wavelike nature of light is summarized. You can see that the frequency and wavelength are inversely proportional—as the wavelength becomes smaller, the frequency becomes larger.

Let's talk about the frequency first. As you know, the frequency of something refers to how often it happens. In this case, the frequency of a light wave is how many times it cycles in one second. To visualize how a light wave cycles, think back about the eel moving in water. A cycle is when the wave (or head of the eel) goes left, then right, and then left again to the point where it began, all while moving in the same direction. The distance that a wave (or the eel) travels while completing one cycle is called the wavelength. You could actually think of frequency as how many wavelengths fit into one second. Wavelength and frequency are aspects of a wave that are *always* related to each other based on the speed of the wave.

Think back to the picture of the eel swimming in water. It is swimming at a certain speed, which determines how long it takes to get from point A to point B. Let's say the eel's speed stays the same but the wavelength gets smaller; that means the eel will get from A to B in the same amount of time, but it will fit in more wavelengths over that distance (more left/right/left/right movement) because the wavelengths are smaller. Since frequency is the number of wavelengths cycled per second, this means the frequency will go up. That is how these two attributes of light—frequency and wavelength—are related: through the speed at which the light is moving (to be discussed in a moment).

Photons of Light and Planck's Constant

Next question: How is it that the energy of light is related to its frequency and wavelength? The answer: Quantum mechanics—specifically, something called "quanta" or a photon of light. In keeping to my promise not to create a physics textbook, we're not going to do a deep dive into quantum mechanics, but the basic idea is that light exists in discrete particles called "photons." In other words, if you were to zoom in on a beam of light to see its most refined, incremental components, you would see a photon, or a single electromagnetic wave, as illustrated in figure 2.1.[11]

In 1900 the German scientist Max Planck proposed that light was made up of discrete photons of a certain energy (making photons particles) that had a wavelength and frequency corresponding to that energy (making photons waves). And what made all of Planck's math work for this seemingly bizarre theory? Planck's constant, of course! This is a number (just like pi, or π, in geometry) that describes the relationship between the energy and frequency of light as shown in this simple equation (I promise, it's the only equation in the whole book):

$$E = hf = \frac{hc}{\lambda}$$

Let's walk through this equation. E is the energy of a photon of light. Remember, when I say *photon*, I am talking about the smallest increment of light as if I were saying *a particle* or *a piece of light*. Planck's constant is h and f is the frequency, so multiplying them together gives E. The higher the E of a photon, the higher its f since h is a constant.[12] In the last part of the equation, c is the speed of light (discussed below), and λ is the wavelength of the photon, thus showing mathematically how wavelength and frequency are related based on speed.

Not long after Planck's postulation in 1900, there was a growing volume of irrefutable experimental evidence that his constant (which was not self-named—he was much more unassuming than that) indeed described the true nature of light. Now, more than one hundred years later, we still rely on the validity of Planck's constant for almost all our modern technology, from communication systems to medical equipment.

Speed of Light

In the last section, we introduced one more aspect of light that is also a fundamental constant of the known scientific universe: the speed of light.[13] How fast is a photon of light actually moving? As it turns out, light moves faster than anything else known in the entire universe. *Nothing we know of moves faster than light.* There is wonderful gospel relevance to this scientific maxim!

Prior to the determination that light moves at a finite speed, it was thought to move instantaneously from one point to the next. Once the speed of light was experimentally proven (now many, many times over), its relevance to countless other things expanded. For instance, the actual definition of a meter (the unit of measure for distance) was refined in the early 1980s based on the speed of light, since the latter was taken to be the most absolute fundamental constant and involved meters: the speed of light, c, is 2.99792458 x 10^8 m/s (that's meters per second).[14]

One last point regarding c is that a light-year is the distance that light travels in one year. Ready to feel small? The distance from the earth to the farthest known galaxy in the universe is 13.3 billion light-years.[15] In other words, it takes 13.3 billion years for light to get from there to Earth. Here are a few other interesting data points on the speed of light; specifically, here is how long it takes for light to travel the following distances:

- 1 foot → 1.0×10^{-9} seconds
  = 1 nanosecond
- around Earth's equator → 0.134 seconds
- from the moon to Earth → 1.3 seconds
- from the sun to Earth → 8.3 minutes
- from the nearest galaxy to Earth → 25,000 years
- across the Milky Way → 100,000 years

Electromagnetic Spectrum

Since we have established that light is broken down into individual pieces called photons and that a photon has a certain energy related to its frequency and wavelength, we are now ready to put this all together in an electromagnetic spectrum. Light is electromagnetic radiation, so all known types of light are represented by mapping out a spectrum (or range) of allowable energies/frequencies/wavelengths. Because these three attributes of light are all interrelated through Planck's constant and the speed of light (also a constant), it doesn't really matter which of them we choose for defining the range of our electromagnetic spectrum; typically, a spectrum will show all three. This is what we have in the spectrum in figure 2.2.

Looking at the electromagnetic spectrum, you will notice the range of energies/frequencies/wavelengths (we will simply call these "energies" from now on, knowing that these three attributes are always interrelated) actually visible to the human eye is very small. This has important implications when considering spiritual light because it shows that almost all the light we are able to scientifically detect and use is completely undetectable with the natural senses of our physical bodies.

All light with energies below that of visible light is what we call "nonionizing"—such light is basically harmless to humans but extremely useful in many technological ways, from transmitting communications to rapidly heating food (microwaves). The light with energies above that of visible light is potentially damaging to humans, from the ultraviolet (UV) rays of the sun that can cause sunburn to the X-rays and gamma rays that, with prolonged or intense exposure, can destroy or mutate cells, thereby causing cancer. How this high-energy light affects us will be a topic of discussion in chapter 3, when we discuss the sensing of light.

Figure 2.2 also shows a final aspect of light on the electromagnetic spectrum—the energy of light that is used for certain communication technologies. How information is actually encoded within the light of a given energy is something we will discuss in chapter 5. For now, note that when you tune your radio to different FM or AM stations, you are adjusting your antennae to pick up light of a certain energy (or frequency). Your radio then processes that light, extracting the information that has been embedded within it.

Where Does Light Come From?

It was mentioned above that light cannot be stored. The next question then is, Where does light actually come from? There are many methods for generating light, each with a variety of unique mechanisms. We will briefly discuss the three most common methods for light emission: thermal radiation (incandescence), electric discharge, and luminescence.

Thermal radiation

Let's start with the process that has brought the world most of its visible light: thermal radiation. The basic idea behind thermal radiation is that when an object is hot (i.e., it has a lot of thermal energy), it will release some of its excess energy in the form of light. Note that thermal radiation is the primary reason the sun radiates light and a fire is visible. Thermal radiation is also how electric light bulbs worked up until the revolution in high-efficiency lighting started to take over in the twenty-first century. When referring specifically to visible light emission by thermal radiation, we typically denote this process as "incandescence."

In short, when something hot emits light, that is thermal radiation. When that light is visible, we call that thermal radiation incandescence. All lamps, fire, sunlight, and the first hundred years of light bulbs generate visible light by incandescence.[16]

Electric discharge

Another method for generating light is by electric discharge. As electrons travel between two electrodes, they interact with gas molecules that then emit light. One of the most common electric discharge methods is called "electric arc," which is the mechanism behind the lightning we see during a storm.[17] In the case of lightning, the electrodes are the sky and the ground, and as electrons travel through the air between them, they interact with the nitrogen- and oxygen-rich atmosphere, leading to light emission (a visible lightning strike). The first successful electric lighting method was based on the arc lamp, which established an electric arc through the air between two carbon electrodes. More modern sources of visible light from electric discharge include gas-discharge lamps such as fluorescent and neon lamps.

Remember, the flow of electrons (electric current) does not, in and of itself, generate light. It is the interaction with gas molecules in the space between two electrodes that leads to the light emission. This is best managed by establishing the electric current inside a controlled environment, such as a glass tube (think about the fluorescent and neon lights), that can be filled with a certain gas. As the electrons interact with molecules of the gas, energy is exchanged, molecules/atoms are ionized (i.e., they experience an increase or decrease in energy), and some of that energy difference is emitted as light.[18]

Luminescence

One final method that will be mentioned for the generation of light is luminescence. Of the three methods considered here, this is by far the most varied in its mechanisms for producing light. By definition, luminescence is the emission of light because of something other than heat (to distinguish it from thermal radiation). What, then, could the something be that is causing the emission? Here are just a few examples:

- *Chemiluminescence.* Light emission resulting from a chemical reaction. Popular example: glow sticks![19]

- *Photoluminescence.* Light emission resulting from the absorption of photons. In a way, this is the reemission of light but at a lower energy.[20] Basically, you shine light of a certain energy on a material or substance, and light of a different energy comes out as a result. There are many examples of using photoluminescence, from scientific to artistic applications, including fluorescent clothing that glows under a black light (note: fluorescence is a type of photoluminescence).

- *Electroluminescence.* Light emission resulting from an electric current flowing through a material, not to be confused with electric arc sources that involve light emission from an electric current flowing through a gas (see discussion above). The most common use is in the form of light-emitting diodes (LEDs). An LED is a semiconductor[21] device that converts electricity flowing through it into light by causing the electrons to lose a very specific amount of their energy as they pass through the device (and that lost energy is converted into light that is emitted from the surface of the material). Because semiconductor materials can be carefully designed, LEDs are able to emit light of a very specific energy (such as red, green, and now, even blue).[22]

- *Bioluminescence.* Light emission resulting from a biochemical reaction in a living organism. This is often seen as a subcategory of chemiluminescence that occurs within a biological organism. The compound found in organisms that bioluminesce is generically referred to as a "luciferin."[23] Upon reaction of the luciferin with a certain enzyme (produced by the organism), energy is released in the form of light. You're likely familiar with several examples, including glowworms and fireflies.

Perhaps the most fascinating fact about luminescence is that it shows how light can be generated from *any* source of energy. Actually, this is true for all three of the methods discussed; thermal radiation is the conversion of heat energy to light, and electric discharge is the conversion of electrical energy (electrons flowing through a gas) to light. The best way to summarize this is that light is generated through the conversion of some form of energy. Later in this book, these underlying physics principles will be applied to the generation of spiritual light, in one form dubbed "spiritualuminescence." If there is a source of energy and some mechanism for converting that energy to light, then we know, based on the laws of physics, that light can be generated.

Fundamental Constants

For this next section, I'd like to take a brief sidestep to point out something that has come up a few times in this chapter thus far: the existence of fundamental constants. Isn't it such a marvel that so many physical and biological processes in the universe can be understood using constants? Take pi (π) for example—a single number based on the relationship of the circumference and diameter of a circle. Since its first definition over two thousand years ago, π has become the most ubiquitous of scientific constants, proving key to virtually all fields of science, from electromagnetism (light) to cosmology. We even celebrate π's significance each year on Pi Day: March 14 (03-14)—a day that is cleverly correlated with the first three digits of π (3.14) and results in massive celebratory consumption of the delicious baked version of "pi."

In addition to π, other mathematical or scientific constants have been discovered or defined over the years. Some of these are considered fundamental physical constants for being universal in nature and time (they do not change and hence are constant). Yet, there is some disagreement as to exactly which constants meet all qualifications and theories to be considered fundamental. Here is a list of some of the most prominent of the physical constants:

- speed of light: $c = 2.99792458 \times 10^8$ m/s
- Planck's constant: $h = 4.135667662 \times 10^{-15}$ eV·s
- gravitational constant: $G = 6.67408 \times 10^{-11}$ m³/kg·s²
- magnetic constant: $\mu_0 = 4\pi \times 10^{-7}$ N/A²
- electric constant: $\varepsilon_0 = 8.854187817 \times 10^{-12}$ F/m
- elementary electron charge: $q = e = 1.602176565 \times 10^{-19}$ C
- mass of an electron: $m_0 = 9.10938291 \times 10^{-31}$ kg

The list could go on, but this gives you an idea of how many fundamental forces in nature manifest physical constants in their operation. Gravity, electricity, magnetism—all are invisible forces with very measurable and tangible effects. In a way, light brings each of these forces together since light itself is the combination of magnetic and electric fields (electromagnetic radiation) and is affected by gravity. Einstein's theory of general relativity actually focuses on how space and time are distorted by gravity and shows how gravity can bend light, which is another evidence of the interrelation of these forces.

The existence of these physical constants affirms the majesty of God's creations. I find the presence of constants to be a reassuring and comforting sign of God's *constancy*. There is order in our glorious world, and we have been able to detect it even with our finite and imperfect means. "Consider the lilies of the field, how they grow; they toil not, neither do they spin," the Savior taught (Matthew 6:28; see Luke 12:27). This scripture is a reflection of God's attention to the finest details in our universe. We know the Creation is one of the three pillars of eternity, along with the Fall and the Atonement,[24] and our small scientific peek into the grandeur of the Creator's work is awe-inspiring! Consider what we learn from King Benjamin, Alma, and Moroni, respectively, about God and his creations:

> Believe in God; believe that he is, and that he created all things, both in heaven and in earth; believe that he has all wisdom, and all power, both in heaven and in earth; believe that man doth not comprehend all the things which the Lord can comprehend. (Mosiah 4:9)

> The scriptures are laid before thee, yea, and all things denote there is a God; yea, even the earth, and all things that are upon the face of it, yea, and its motion, yea, and also all the planets which move in their regular form do witness that there is a Supreme Creator. (Alma 30:44)

> For do we not read that God is the same yesterday, today, and forever, and in him there is no variableness neither shadow of changing? (Mormon 9:9)

Among all the things I can think of that are constants associated with God, what stands out most is the eternal constancy of his love for his children and his endless offering of joy (see 2 Nephi 2:25).[25] As President Russell M. Nelson taught, "Just as the Savior offers peace that 'passeth all understanding,' He also offers an intensity, depth, and breadth of joy that defy human logic or mortal comprehension. . . . *His joy is constant*, assuring us that our 'afflictions shall be but a small moment' and be consecrated to our gain."[26] There are spiritual, even heavenly, constants that cannot be measured by scientific instruments or spelled out in mathematical theories; yet they are there. We know it by how we feel, by who we are, by how others influence us, and, interestingly, by how we can change.

We have now established a reasonable foundation in the core physical aspects of light. The purpose of the remainder of this book is to build on this foundation by discussing some ideas of how spiritual light operates and by exploring evidences and doctrines of light throughout scripture. I hope to do this in a way that may be edifying and uplifting in order to expand our understanding of God and his purposes. I did not write this to suggest a definitive theory for the doctrine of spiritual light. I imagine that the textbooks of heaven have record of all the equations and constants governing spiritual light and how it is sourced, encoded, and sensed. Our task in this life is not to re-create such texts (to do so would result in woefully inadequate renditions) but to seek, embrace, and discern all the spiritual light that we can. Just as Dr. Feynman noted about his doctoral physics students, it's unlikely any of us truly understands exactly how light works; yet, from a spiritual point of view, we certainly can become more adept at harnessing its power.

Notes

1. Richard P. Feynman, *QED: The Strange Theory of Light and Matter* (Princeton, NJ: Princeton University Press, 1988).
2. The exceptions to this are light sources designed to send light in all directions, such as the light bulb. In that case, the light is being emitted without directional control. This is true for all filament-based light sources (such as the incandescent bulb). In fact, if you look closely at the end of a flashlight that uses a bulb

(rather than one with a light-emitting diode—LED—source), you will see that there is a conical mirror used to direct the light into a beam. More modern LED flashlights no longer require such mirrors because the light emits perpendicularly from the surface of the flat source—great for flashlights but problematic for light bulbs! For this reason, LED light bulbs have other aspects in their design to help spread the light into all directions (either by using multiple LED sources positioned in the bulb or by coating the bulb with a material that spreads the light in random directions).

3. The physiological process that enables sight will be briefly discussed in chapter 8, but it is worth noting here that we achieve sight by detecting how light interacts with something. The importance of the directionality of the light is further shown by how it is refracted upon its passing through the lens and its eventual impacting of the retina at the back of the eye. Nerves in the eye then process the details of the light that has hit them, resolving the light into an image based on the direction it came from, its energy, and its intensity.

4. This force, whether attractive or repulsive, between two or more electrically charged bodies is known as the Coulomb force. The magnitude of this electrostatic force is inversely proportional to the square of the separation between the charges (i.e., as the charged bodies get closer together, the force attracting or repelling them gets stronger).

5. The illustration in figure 2.1 provides further details regarding how an electric field and a magnetic field are combined to form a photon of light. Each photon (or piece) of light is made up of these inextricably related fields, which are offset from each other by 90 degrees (i.e., orthogonally combined). They do not separate from each other. They propagate, or move, together in the same direction and at the same rate/speed/frequency. The illustration makes it seem as if the photon of light were just a standing wave (i.e., something that is not moving in space), spreading from the source (a flashlight) to wherever it hits something; this is not accurate because the photon of light is always in motion with a very specific location at any given point of time (though this is governed by the uncertainty principle of quantum physics).

6. Just as magnetic and electric fields have a certain strength when they are on their own, when combined to form an electromagnetic wave, the wave will also have a certain strength in the form of energy. If you have ever handled a strong magnet (such as one made from neodymium), then you have experienced the difference in strength between a weak magnetic field (common refrigerator

magnets) and a strong magnetic field. The same is true for light. The strength of the photon of light is based on its energy. An interesting thing to note is that two photons of light could have very different energy (like the weak and strong magnets), but both would still travel at the same speed. You experience this every day as you detect different colors—each color is a distinct energy of light.

7. The *e* refers to the elementary charge of an electron. It is also often referred to as *q* rather than *e*. Physically, *e* is the amount of electrical charge in a single electron (the smallest, most fundamental unit of electricity). In its most basic definition, the electron volt (eV) is the amount of energy lost or gained by an electron as it moves through one volt of electric potential difference. That definition may not help with understanding why eV is used for describing the energy of light, but keep in mind that the generation and absorption of light is almost entirely governed by electrons losing or gaining energy. When an electron that is within a solid piece of material loses energy, that energy must go somewhere (we say that it is conserved). One of the most common places for the energy to go is into the generation of a photon of light. What will the energy of that photon be? It will be precisely the amount of energy (in eV) that the electron lost. It works similarly for the absorption of light by a material; one of the most common ways that a photon of light is absorbed is by an electron gaining the energy of the photon.

8. Ever wonder why you often stagger the orientation of batteries when putting them into electronics—positive side up, then positive side down, and so forth? That's because you're adding them in what is called "series," which means you are increasing the voltage by 1.5 V with each additional battery. Because electric potential (voltage) has a certain directionality to it (as we discussed above with positive and negative charges), the batteries must be installed properly in order to realize the increase in voltage. One point of clarification here regarding energy in batteries is that while voltage is a form of electric potential energy (which does indeed increase when batteries are added in series), when we talk about battery energy, we are most often talking about the power (voltage times the current) multiplied by time—in other words, we are not just talking about the electric potential but also about the amount of electricity that is able to be delivered in a given increment of time. In some applications, the energy of a battery source is increased by adding the batteries in the same direction to boost the current (flow of electrons or electricity) since the application has higher demands on current than on electric potential.

9. It is worth noting that the first concrete elucidation of how photons have momentum but no mass was in Albert Einstein's explanation of the photoelectric effect. It had been observed that when light hits the surface of certain materials, electrons (referred to as photoelectrons) may be emitted from the material. However, the electrons would only be emitted if the light were of sufficiently high energy, the threshold for which was material-dependent. Prior to Einstein's postulation, the prevailing theory was that light is purely a continuous wave, which would suggest that with enough intensity and time, it could eventually cause electrons to be removed from a material—but this was not the case. Einstein was able to prove that light is actually made up of discrete quantum packets (quanta or photons) with their own distinct energy. Shining more of these individual photons (i.e., increased intensity), all of which had energies below that needed for electron emissions, would produce no photoelectrons from a material; but increasing the energy of the photons until some were above the threshold for the material would produce the photoelectrons. This dependence on the individual energy of discrete photons was the core of Einstein's theory of the photoelectric effect, for which he was awarded the Nobel Prize in Physics in 1921. The following sentence from Einstein's March 1905 scientific paper presenting his explanation of the photoelectric effect is noteworthy: "According to the assumption to be contemplated here, when a light ray is spreading from a point, the energy is not distributed continuously over ever-increasing spaces, but consists of a finite number of energy quanta that are localized in points in space, move without dividing, and can be absorbed or generated only as a whole." See https://npr.org/2005/03/17/4538324/albert-einsteins-year-of-miracles-light-theory.

10. There are many great examples of this available on the internet, such as https://youtube.com/watch?v=RgJCxN3ShbY.

11. This particular aspect of quantum mechanics may actually be fairly logical to some readers—namely, that light comes in specific increments called photons. However, it was not obvious based on the widely accepted scientific knowledge of the nineteenth century, when light was considered to be purely a wave that fills space, unable to be broken down or limited by some discrete component (the photon).

12. For the extraordinarily inquisitive reader that may be wondering what the value of Planck's constant is, I will provide it here in units of eV times seconds to satiate your curiosity: $4.135667662 \times 10^{-15}$ eV·s.

13. Determination of the speed of light played a big role in Einstein's development of his theory of relativity. In fact, it is this constant that interrelates space and time, including how these aspects of our universe depend on each other. We won't delve into the details of spacetime and Einstein's theories of relativity, but it is critical to point out that light is related to space and time. This is something worth pondering when considering the nature of spiritual light.

14. The constant c refers to light's speed in a vacuum (such as outer space), which is defined as a space that is void of nearly all particles. You might be wondering if this speed then changes as light moves through earth's atmosphere, and the answer is yes. There is a slight reduction in the speed that light moves if not in a vacuum, but it is a very minor reduction that is only detectable with the most advanced instrumentation.

15. Clara Moskowitz, "Farthest Known Galaxy in the Universe Discovered," *Space.com*, November 2012, https://space.com/18502-farthest-galaxy-discovery-hubble-photos.html.

16. The problem is that incandescent light sources emit far more than just visible light. This is one of the reasons for the phasing out of the incandescent light bulb—most of its emission, and thus most of the electrical power it consumes, is in the infrared light (not visible) range, making its efficiency for generating visible light quite low.

17. An important point of clarification is that lightning is more finely thought of as an electric spark. This distinction (electric spark rather than electric arc) is based on the fact that lightning is a form of abrupt electrical discharge rather than sustained electrical discharge. For electric arcs, the discharge (or flow of electricity) across the dielectric medium (whatever is separating the two electrodes) is sustained, typically through applying a certain amount of electricity to the system.

18. Note that for fluorescent lights, the light emitted by the gas molecules is actually ultraviolet light (high energy, not visible). Therefore, these types of light sources have their glass tubes coated with a material (a phosphor) that will fluoresce, meaning it will convert the ultraviolet light that hits it into light in the lower energy range of visible light.

19. For the reader with deep chemical curiosity, the most common reaction within a glow stick involves hydrogen peroxide (contained in the fragile inner tube that you break to activate the stick) and diphenyl oxalate that is mixed with a

dye. The reaction is exothermic (based on one of the byproducts, peroxyacid, decomposing to carbon dioxide), meaning it releases thermal energy, which the dye molecules absorb and rerelease in the form of light (thermal radiation).

20. This form of light generation is very useful in the characterization of various chemicals, from liquids to solids. The photoluminescence of a given material when light of a certain energy is shined on it provides a great deal of information about the atoms/molecules that make up the material or substance.

21. A semiconductor material has an electrical conductivity (a measure of how well electricity flows through it) that can be controllably varied, unlike a conductor that always has high conductivity and an insulator that always has very low conductivity. Tuning the conductivity of semiconductors, such as silicon, is at the very heart of how transistors work in computers (transistors are the devices responsible for the computing revolution of the past sixty years).

22. In 2014 the Nobel Prize in Physics was awarded to three researchers "for the invention of efficient blue light-emitting diodes." The reason that blue LEDs are of such significance is because they provide the missing link for creating white light sources entirely from LEDs, which is substantially more efficient than other light sources.

23. Interestingly, the Latin root for the term *luciferin* is *lucifer*, which is translated as "light bringer" or "morning star."

24. See Bruce R. McConkie, "The Three Pillars of Eternity" (Brigham Young University devotional, 17 February 1981). The talk can be found at https://speeches.byu.edu/talks/bruce-r-mcconkie_three-pillars-eternity.

25. See David A. Grandy, "Physical Light and the Light of Christ," *BYU Studies Quarterly* 53, no. 4 (2014): 7–36. Grandy provides a wonderful exposition on the speed of light, its vast implications (including on spacetime), and its connection to, and representation of, the constancy of God's love. Overall, the article gives a very compelling description of the grandeur of light and its role in the cosmos.

26. Russell M. Nelson, "Joy and Spiritual Survival," *Ensign*, November 2016, 81; emphasis added.

Spiritual Body Radiation

Every man, every person radiates what he or she is. Every person is a recipient of radiation. The Savior was conscious of that. . . . He was conscious of the radiation from the individual. And to a degree so are you, and so am I. It is what we are and what we radiate that affects the people around us.[1]

—President David O. McKay

One of the most famed teachings from Jesus Christ's New Testament ministry comes from the Sermon on the Mount when he instructed, "Let your light so shine before men, that they may see your good works, and glorify your Father which is in heaven" (Matthew 5:16). This teaching from the Master is part commandment (*let* your light shine) and part doctrine (living the gospel results in light that shines from you and affects others). This chapter will explore how we radiate light, while the next chapter will focus on the detection of that light by others.

Remember in school when you were taught that a white object reflects all light, whereas one that is black absorbs all light? I learned this from the school of hard knocks by growing up in the blistering heat of the Arizona sun. It didn't take much of my deductive powers to figure out that black leather seats are not ideal when climbing into a car that's been parked in the sun. I also figured out pretty quickly that asphalt and bare feet don't play well together in the middle of summer! All of that absorption of light caused anything dark-colored to heat up in a way that pale-colored things would not. We need to dissect this idea of how different objects absorb different amounts of light in order to understand how we all emit light—otherwise known as radiation. This idea builds off our discussions of the sources of light in chapter 2, which included thermal radiation—a method for light emission that we will briefly revisit below.

Blackbody Radiation

In the mid-1800s, scientists were earnestly working to figure out the physical nature of light (electromagnetic radiation). One observation that became of great importance to the German scientist, Gustav Kirchhoff, was that the state-of-the-art radiation detectors of his day suggested that everything—animate or inanimate, living or dead—emits light so long as it is not at absolute zero temperature (i.e., completely absent of any heat). This is different from zero degrees Fahrenheit or zero degrees Celsius; absolute zero (with scientific units of Kelvin) is the point at which there is no heat whatsoever (this would be equivalent to -273.15°C or -459.67°F). Kirchhoff's observation suggested that everything in the universe that is not at absolute zero is emitting light. This troubled some scientists of his day because it unraveled the previous assumption that a scientifically termed *blackbody* would not emit any light (i.e., would have no radiation).

A blackbody is the scientific term for an object that is a perfect absorber. Picture this as something that takes in all of the light that hits it without any light reflecting off of it. A red-colored object absorbs all visible light except for red, which it reflects;[2] the same is true for objects that are blue, orange, yellow, and so forth. The color of an object is determined by the light that it reflects, with white being a reflection of all visible light and black being an absorption of all visible light and a reflection of no light. Of course, when determining the color of an object we are only focusing on the very small portion of the electromagnetic spectrum that is visible to our physical eyes, whereas a true blackbody is one that theoretically would absorb *all* wavelengths/energies of light that hit it, visible and invisible.

Scientists realized that even such a perfect absorber of all impinging light would *still* emit radiation. This revelation was startling and didn't make sense to them. They wondered where the radiated light could be coming from if the light that was hitting the blackbody wasn't bouncing off of it. Kirchhoff was the first to answer this question and define this concept, which he dubbed "blackbody radiation," saying that even a perfect black-body will still emit light as a result of its thermal energy. Basically, when an object (including a person) is at a temperature above absolute zero (which all things are, even those at the frigid peaks of Antarctica), it will emit light in a process known as thermal radiation. *Thermal* implies that the energy for emitting the light results from its temperature, and *radiation* is what happens to that energy (it turns into light, i.e., electromagnetic radiation).

Blackbody radiation is something that occurs regardless of the visible color of an object—it is a color-independent effect—and is scientifically based wholly on temperature. In other words, the conceptual blackbody was just used as a scientific extreme; in reality, *everything* in the known universe emits the so-called blackbody radiation in the form of thermal energy. As an object becomes hotter, there will be a noticeable change in the blackbody radiation that it emits. Sometimes such radiation is visible, but typically it is not. An example of this visible radiation would be a black iron fireplace poker. When plunged into the heart of a blazing fire, the poker will heat up and eventually begin to visibly glow an orange-reddish color, as shown in the picture in figure 3.1(a). This change in color is purely a result of the blackbody radiation fueled by the heat from the fire. It has nothing to do with reflected or absorbed light, which is what is causing the remainder of the handle to be a visible black color. The area that is bright orange is still actually black in color, but the visible blackbody radiation overpowers the typical color determination from absorbed/reflected light.

When an object or person is at room temperature (approximately 73 degrees Fahrenheit, 23 degrees Celsius, or 296 Kelvin), the majority of its

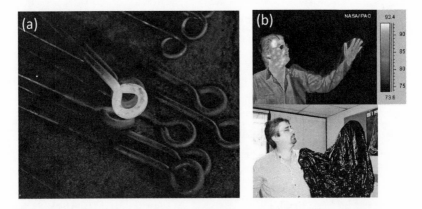

Figure 3.1. (a) Picture of fire pokers. Heat causes one to glow an orange-red color in a visible display of blackbody radiation (image by fir0002flagstaffotos@gmail.com Canon 20D + Tamron 28-75mm f/2.8 - Own work, GFDL 1.2, https://commons.wiki media.org/w/index.php?curid=136199). (b) Image of a person taken by an infrared camera compared to the same frame with a typical camera. (See spiritualphysicsof light.com.)

blackbody radiation is in the infrared energy range (0.00124 eV to 1.7 eV). Infrared light is just beyond the visible energy range, so our eyes can't see it. However, detectors like infrared cameras have been made that can selectively sense infrared light. An example image from an infrared camera is shown in figure 3.1(b). You can clearly detect the outline of a person, but the distribution of colors is based strictly on the infrared blackbody radiation.

Spiritual Body Radiation

Having established the scientific reality that all people and objects emit radiation, let's now consider the spiritual aspects. If an object emits light because it has thermal energy, it seems reasonable to conclude that our spirits emit a type of spiritual light when they have an associated spiritual energy. After all, "there is no such thing as immaterial matter. All spirit is matter, but it is more fine or pure, and can only be discerned by purer eyes; we cannot see it; but when our bodies are purified we shall see that it is all matter" (Doctrine and Covenants 131:7–8). Indeed, it is a realistic deduction that the "more fine or pure" construct of our spirits would also emit their own form of light based on some form of energy and be able to feel, or in some instances even see, the spiritual light emitted from others. While we understand much about what type of light our physical eyes are able to detect, we obviously have no scientific information about what our spiritual eyes, or spirits, can detect. This will be a discussion for the next chapter, but it is helpful to begin thinking now about the ability of our spirits to detect other forms of light that are not necessarily visible to the physical eye. Consider these powerful and insightful teachings from Elder Parley P. Pratt:

> As the mind passes the boundaries of the visible world, and enters upon the confines of the more refined and subtle elements, it finds itself associated with certain substances in themselves invisible to our gross organs, but clearly manifested to our intellect by their tangible operations and effects.
>
> The purest, most refined and subtle of all these substances—is that substance called the Holy Spirit.
>
> It is in its less refined particles, the physical light which reflects from the sun, moon and stars, and other substances; and by reflection on the eye makes visible the truths of the outward world.[3]

I will use the term *spiritual light* from here on out to refer to a form of light that may not be visible to the natural eye or detectable by scientific equipment but is radiated and even sensed in some fashion by our spirits.

We Are Always Radiating

Before exploring how our spiritual light radiation may be related to our righteousness, I want to note that *everyone radiates some form of spiritual light*. Perhaps those who are righteous radiate a greater variety of spiritual light (broader spectrum), or radiate more intensity, or have different information encoded within. Regardless of the distinction between radiation from a righteous person versus a wicked person, the reality is that everyone radiates something. From that radiation, understanding can be gleaned from those who receive the radiation.

There may have been no prophet more fascinated with this doctrine of radiation than President David O. McKay. Here are a few of his powerful teachings on the subject (which were quoted in part at the beginning of this chapter):

> Every person who lives in this world wields an influence, whether for good or for evil. It is not what he says alone, it is not alone what he does. It is what he is. Every man, every person radiates what he or she is. Every person is a recipient of radiation. The Savior was conscious of that. Whenever he came into the presence of an individual, he sensed that radiation—whether it was the woman of Samaria with her past life; whether it was the woman who was to be stoned or the men who were to stone her; whether it was the statesman, Nicodemus, or one of the lepers. He was conscious of the radiation from the individual. And to a degree so are you, and so am I. It is what we are and what we radiate that affects the people around us.
>
> . . . If we think noble thoughts, if we encourage and cherish noble aspirations, there will be that radiation when we meet people, especially when we associate with them.
>
> . . . The Savior set us the example, always calm, always controlled, radiating something which people could feel as they passed. . . . God help us to radiate strength, control, love, charity, which is another name for love, consideration, best wishes for all human beings.[4]

> Every moment of life you are changing to a degree the lives of the whole world. . . . So, it's not the surroundings, it isn't the positions; the thing that will influence [others] in this world, are personalities. No matter what you are people will feel and recognize this. You radiate, you can't hide it. You may pretend something else, but that will not affect people.[5]

The English writer Thomas Carlyle referred to those who have a powerful, positive influence on the world around them as "light-fountains."[6] So, it's not just that we should recognize that we all radiate spiritual light, but we should learn to turn this radiation into a light-fountain of comfort, compassion, and charity to all around us. How this spiritual body radiation may actually work will be our next consideration.

Hypotheses on the Radiation of Spiritual Light

This is a good place to remind the reader that most of the forthcoming concepts are my personal interpretations; my hypotheses, if you will. I am going to offer two perspectives regarding what governs the radiation of spiritual light and the roles of the Light of Christ and the Holy Ghost in this process. Not only are these suppositional, they are also not in the required learning for exaltation! I love President Gordon B. Hinckley's comment about not getting lost in the finer (and almost always subjectively interpreted) details of doctrine: "I do not worry whether the heavenly gates swing or slide. I am only concerned that they open."[7]

Why bother then to share my perspectives? Because, as a scientist, I have come to appreciate the great value of exploring a variety of hypotheses when seeking to understand a scientific problem or mystery. When pondering on a given subject, considering other ideas and interpretations can lead to the development of a sounder hypothesis and more understanding. So, please, consider the ensuing discussion as simply my hypotheses on the roles of the Light of Christ and the Holy Ghost with respect to the generation of spiritual light. What is certain is the value of studying and applying the doctrine of light, as President Dieter F. Uchtdorf taught: "The more we understand and apply the doctrinal concept of light, the more we can guard against spiritual sicknesses that afflict or trouble us on every side and hand, and the better we can serve as energetic, courageous, caring . . . servants and disciples of our beloved and eternal King."[8]

Hypothesis 1: Spiritual energy fuels spiritual light

This first hypothesis is built on the principle that all things were created spiritually before they were created physically (see Moses 3:5), and hence there is some correlation between what we observe physically and what governs things spiritually. In this case, just as blackbody radiation is caused by thermal energy, I draw the correlation that spiritual body radiation would need a source of some type of spiritual energy. This correlation is based purely on what we understand about light scientifically. Light cannot be stored because it is made up of waves that are always in motion. Most sources of visible light have some mechanism for converting electrical energy into photons, such as a battery (energy) powering a light bulb (conversion to photons). The point is, the source of radiated light of any type cannot be from the storage of that light; rather, the source of light must be something that converts a form of energy into the light. In the remaining discussion throughout this book, this scientific principle is assumed to hold true for the generation of spiritual light.

Many scriptures use phrasing such as "receiving light," which I interpret to mean that a person has received the needed spiritual energy to radiate light (hence, the person has received that light). To determine what the spiritual energy source could be, consider the following teachings from scripture and a general conference talk by President Uchtdorf regarding the attainment of light:

> Then spake Jesus again unto them, saying, I am the light of the world: *he that followeth me* shall not walk in darkness, but shall have the light of life. (John 8:12; emphasis added)

> *He that loveth his brother* abideth in the light, and there is none occasion of stumbling in him. (1 John 2:10; emphasis added)

> That which is of God is light; and he that receiveth light, and *continueth in God*, receiveth more light; and that light groweth brighter and brighter until the perfect day. (Doctrine and Covenants 50:24; emphasis added)

> Every time you turn your hearts to God in humble prayer, you experience His light. Every time you seek His word and will in the scriptures, the light grows in brightness. Every time you notice someone in need and sacrifice your own comfort to reach out in love, the light expands and swells. Every time you reject temptation and choose purity, every time you seek or extend forgiveness, every time you courageously testify of truth, the light chases away darkness and attracts others who are also seeking light and truth.[9]

These teachings emphasize that spiritual light comes from, generally speaking, keeping the commandments of God and seeking to become more like him. The first two excerpts reflect what are popularly known as the two great commandments, namely to "love the Lord thy God with all thy heart, and with all thy soul, and with all thy mind" (Matthew 22:37) and to "love thy neighbor as thyself" (22:39): "On these two commandments hang all the law and the prophets" (22:40). It is our closeness to God, through obedience to the commandments and repentance from sin, that brings us the spiritual energy to fuel the radiation of spiritual light. As summarized by Elder Robert D. Hales:

> So it is with spiritual light. It must be renewed in us on a regular basis. We must generate it day by day, thought by thought, and with daily righteous action if we are to keep the darkness of the adversary away.
>
> When I was a boy, I used to ride my bicycle home from basketball practice at night. I would connect a small pear-shaped generator to my bicycle tire. Then as I pedaled, the tire would turn a tiny rotor, which produced electricity and emitted a single, welcome beam of light. It was a simple but effective mechanism. But I had to pedal to make it work! I learned quickly that if I stopped pedaling my bicycle, the light would go out. I also learned that when I was "anxiously engaged" in pedaling, the light would become brighter and the darkness in front of me would be dispelled.
>
> The generation of spiritual light comes from daily spiritual pedaling. It comes from praying, studying the scriptures, fasting, and serving—from living the gospel and obeying the commandments.[10]

Now that we have an idea of where spiritual energy comes from, what then is the spiritual energy that a person obtains to fuel radiation of spiritual light? One thought would be that it is the Light of Christ, which is "given to every man, that he may know good from evil" (Moroni 7:16) and "lighteth every man that cometh into the world" (Doctrine and Covenants 93:2). Many think of the Light of Christ solely as someone's conscience; while there is no doubt it is indeed that, it is so very much more. Reviewing just a few scriptures about the Light of Christ reveals the incredible scope of this eternal power:

> He that ascended up on high, as also he descended below all things, in that he comprehended all things, that he might be in all and through all things, the light of truth.

Which truth shineth. This is the light of Christ. As also he is in the sun, and the light of the sun, and the power thereof by which it was made. . . .

The light which is in all things, which giveth life to all things, which is the law by which all things are governed, even the power of God who sitteth upon his throne, who is in the bosom of eternity, who is in the midst of all things. (Doctrine and Covenants 88:6–7, 13)

It is essential to recognize that the Light of Christ is one of the most encompassing and incredible powers of which we are aware. I believe that the Light of Christ is inextricably tied to the atoning sacrifice of Jesus Christ. His infinite Atonement brought the capacity for exaltation to every person that will ever live; hence, all have the opportunity to return to, and even become like, God.

So, the Light of Christ is a power far greater than can possibly be fathomed; yet, it is given to *every* person in the entire world. How is this? At the very least this makes it an implausible candidate for the spiritual energy that fuels radiation of spiritual light, as *all* are given the Light of Christ yet *not all* are radiating the fullness of light that is "the power of God who sitteth upon his throne" (Doctrine and Covenants 88:13). In other words, we just established above that obedience leads to the attainment of more light, but the Light of Christ is spoken of as being given to every person without specific conditions of worthiness (hence, these two attributes are at odds with each other).

While there is no doubt that the Light of Christ is a part of our spiritual light radiation, it does not make sense to consider this power as the sole spiritual energy that actually fuels the radiation. However, what if at least part of the role of the Light of Christ were to convert spiritual energy into spiritual light? It would make sense based on the Light of Christ being given to every person yet also being a source for light of all types.

With the Light of Christ embedded within every soul (the soul being the spirit + the body) that comes "into the world" (John 1:9), and because we know "God is light" (1 John 1:5), I hypothesize that one function of the Light of Christ is to be the spiritual light source within each person's soul— capable of filling us with light *if* we have the spiritual energy to fuel it. Even the most powerful light bulb can be dimmed by controlling the amount of electrical energy that flows through it. So it is with the Light of Christ in our souls: spiritual light will radiate corresponding to the amount of spiritual energy with which it is provided. This presence of the Light of Christ within every soul—providing the capability of completely filling the soul with light—is emblematic of each person's potential for godhood. At any point, the Lord can power the Light of Christ in our souls to provide heavenly guidance; in other words, it is at least one way in which he is always with us. This Light of Christ within us is capable of radiating the very light of God that *is* God and thus represents our potential to become *like* God.

This still leaves our initial question unanswered: What is the spiritual energy that powers greater radiation of spiritual light from the Light of Christ in our souls? I suggest that it is the Holy Ghost.

The Holy Ghost being with us is the key indicator of righteousness. Teachings similar to those we reviewed previously (regarding how we obtain light) can also be found regarding how we obtain the companionship of the Holy Ghost. Just think of the sacrament prayers; we promise to take upon us the name of Christ, always remember him, and keep the commandments "which he has given [us]" (Doctrine and Covenants 20:77). What is promised in return? We will "always have his Spirit to be with [us]" (20:77).

There is a strong potential for confusion when determining what is meant by "Spirit of the Lord" vs. "his Spirit" vs. "Holy Spirit" throughout the scriptures.[11] There are occasions when the title "Spirit of the Lord" is used in reference to the Light of Christ. However, I interpret "his Spirit" referred to in the sacrament prayers as the Holy Ghost because having the Light of Christ (in at least some portion) does not hinge on the qualifications of our righteousness but is given to every person.[12]

Whether the sacrament prayers are referring exclusively to the Holy Ghost or the Spirit of Christ (Light of Christ) is a fact far less significant than our need to ensure we are worthy of the promise! Besides, confusion about the use of the title "Spirit" is, at least in part, related to the strong interworking of the Holy Ghost and Light of Christ. This point was summarized by Daniel K Judd, professor of ancient scripture at BYU, as follows:

The Spirit of Christ [light of Christ] is often confused with the Holy Ghost, the gift of the Holy Ghost, and the spirit personage of Jesus Christ. Some of the confusion obviously comes because terms such as *Spirit of the Lord*, *Spirit of God*, and *Spirit of Christ* are often used interchangeably in both scripture and conversation, and it is often difficult to determine to which personage or gift the passage refers. It is from the prophets of this dispensation that we learn the Spirit of Christ is neither the Holy Ghost, the gift of the Holy Ghost, nor the spirit personage of Jesus Christ, *but it is the primary means by which these entities operate*.[13]

This slight overlap between the titles (and functions) of the Light of Christ and the Holy Ghost led me to conceptualize that the Holy Ghost is the spiritual energy that fuels enhanced radiation from the Light of Christ in our souls. This connection has been taught by President Marion G. Romney and President Brigham Young, respectively, as follows:

The gift of the Holy Ghost confers upon one, as long as [one] is worthy, the right to receive light and truth.[14]

[The Holy Ghost influences people] through the increased rays of that light which lighteth every [person] that cometh into the world.[15]

The closer we are to God, the more profoundly the Holy Ghost will influence our life and bring corresponding radiation from the Light of Christ. Likewise, a decrease in the Holy Ghost's influence (or less yielding thereto) should also lead to a reduction in our radiation. We see evidence for this in the following verses:

And he that repents not, from him *shall be taken even the light which he has received; for my Spirit shall not always strive with man*, saith the Lord of Hosts. (Doctrine and Covenants 1:33; emphasis added)

If you keep not my commandments, the love of the Father shall not continue with you, therefore you shall walk in darkness. (Doctrine and Covenants 95:12)

The shew of their countenance doth witness against them. (Isaiah 3:9)

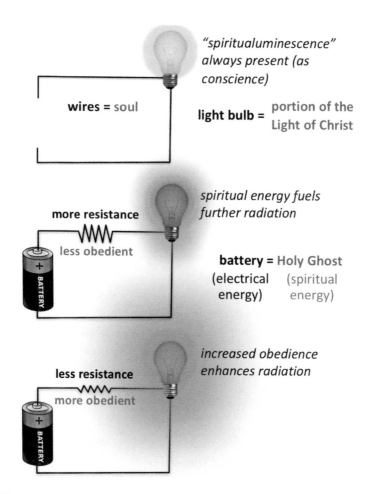

Figure 3.2. Conceptual electrical circuits illustrating one possibility (by analogy) of how spiritual light radiation is powered. We all have a portion of the Light of Christ, which is a perfect light source that is broken down into two parts: (1) a luminescent coating (spiritualuminescence) that is always radiating a small amount of light, like the conscience, and (2) a light bulb that radiates light based on the energy supplied to it. The level of spiritual energy supplied is based on our obedience to, and worthiness of, the Holy Ghost (analogous to the battery in the electrical circuit). (See spiritualphysicsoflight.com.)

Analogy of an electrical light bulb circuit. To summarize this hypothesis of how we radiate spiritual light, I will use an analogy of a simple electrical circuit for a light bulb, as shown in the diagram in figure 3.2. First, let's

43

consider how the electrical circuit works. The battery provides electrical energy (electricity) for the circuit. In order for that electricity to flow, the circuit must form a complete loop from the positive (+) terminal to the negative (-) terminal of the battery. This loop is formed and, as part of the loop, a light bulb has been included so that the electricity will flow through the light bulb. The light bulb itself is designed to give off light as the electricity passes through it. From our discussion in chapter 2, remember that the light bulb is electroluminescent—it generates light from electrical energy (just as an LED does).

If the circuit is nothing more than a battery connected directly to a light bulb, then the light bulb will receive *all* possible electrical energy from the battery and will shine with all its potential brightness. However, typically there is a resistor placed in the circuit to reduce or regulate the amount of energy that is being delivered to the light bulb. Physically, a resistor is composed of a less-than-pure electrical conductor, such as a metal that has some other materials added into it that reduce how well electricity will flow through it. Resistors are extremely useful in electrical circuits because they help tune how much electrical energy will be provided to different portions of a circuit. In our simple circuit, the size of the resistor (how much resistance it has) determines the amount of electrical energy that will reach the light bulb, resulting in a method to tune the brightness of the light that is emitted.

Now let's relate the electrical circuit for the light bulb to the radiation of spiritual light from our souls. The battery represents the Holy Ghost, which provides the spiritual energy for the circuit. The light bulb represents a portion of the Light of Christ, which is in our soul and can generate *all light* if provided with the completely unhampered influence of the Holy Ghost (spiritual energy). This unhampered generation of spiritual light would represent our complete and total yielding of our will to that of the Father. Recall that one of the core missions of the Holy Ghost is to teach and testify of all things regarding God the Father and Jesus Christ (see 3 Nephi 28:11; Ether 12:41; Doctrine and Covenants 42:17). Therefore, if the Holy Ghost's influence upon us is complete, then we would indeed know God and thus would be like him, full of his light—the Light of Christ—and would radiate with full power.

What gauges the actual brightness of the radiated light is the amount of resistance that the spiritual energy from the Holy Ghost experiences in the circuits of our souls. The resistor, then, represents our obedience (generally speaking); greater obedience represents a smaller resistor and lesser obedience represents a larger resistor. As we know, the "natural man is an enemy to God" and must become "submissive" (Mosiah 3:19), which is antonymous to resistive. Since physical resistors are comprised of electrical conductors filled with impurities (the more impurities, the higher the resistance), this part of the analogy is quite compelling. The more temporal impurities we allow into our lives, the greater our resistance to the spiritual energy that can flow from the Holy Ghost.

For years I thought that disobedience limited the *amount of the Holy Ghost* that was able to be with us (even if we had received the gift of the Holy Ghost); but I no longer feel that this is correct. Having only a piece of the Holy Ghost with us doesn't make a lot of sense. I have come to believe that we either have the Holy Ghost with us or we do not. The question is, are we making full use of the spiritual energy from the Holy Ghost's influence—yielding to it above all else? That is determined by our individual obedience, which acts as the resistors in our souls. The book of Alma refers to Ammon and his brethren having a portion of that Spirit dwelling with them (see Alma 17:9; 18:35; 24:8; 40:13; Doctrine and Covenants 71:1), yet I am still inclined to attribute that choice of wording—a portion—to the level of resistance an individual may have that causes the full *power* of the Holy Ghost to be subdued. What's more, the Spirit spoken of by Ammon may well be interpreted to mean the Spirit of Christ or the Light of Christ. Admittedly, this position is highly interpretive and does not compromise the hypothesis of the Holy Ghost being the spiritual energy that fuels our spiritual light—which light is knowledge (see Doctrine and Covenants 93:24, 28) and "a portion of that Spirit [which] dwelleth in [us], which giveth [us] knowledge, and also power according to [our] faith and desires which are in God" (Alma 18:35).

I have chosen obedience as a single example because it encompasses so many other principles of righteousness, but anything that brings us closer to the Lord can be considered a reduction in our resistance (i.e., increased submissiveness to God)—faith, rendering service, and so forth will all have this effect. Conversely, anything that draws us away from the Lord will increase the size of our resistor and suppress the influence of the Holy Ghost, which in turn yields less light for us to radiate. The ever-strived-for "perfect day" (Doctrine and Covenants 50:24) would be a case of complete obedience and total submission to the Lord's will, wherein there would be no resistance to the Holy Ghost, and our spiritual light would be fully powered and would emanate the Light of Christ in its fullness. This is when our whole bodies would be filled with light, and there would be no darkness in us (see Doctrine and Covenants 88:67).

Note that this entire picture of how the Light of Christ and the Holy Ghost operate in our souls to bring us spiritual light is deeply connected to the Atonement of the Lord Jesus Christ. This connection will be explored in detail in chapter 9, but it is important to recognize now that the Savior's Atonement is at the very heart of each of us having the Light of Christ and the ability to emit spiritual light.

There is one other essential feature to this analogy. The Light of Christ (light bulb) cannot be limited to radiating light only when the Holy Ghost (battery/energy) is with us. The scriptures are quite clear that the Light of Christ is given to all and is the steady influence for good within each soul (see Moroni 7:16; Doctrine and Covenants 93:2). Therefore, the analogous light bulb must include some form of luminescent coating that is *always* glowing. Recall that luminescence is the generation of light based on something other than heat; bioluminescence is light from a biological organism, electroluminescence is light from electrical energy, and so forth. Perhaps this coating on our internal light source should be thought of as "spiritualuminescence" since it would be radiating light based on the Spirit of Christ and his influence on, and attention to, our spirits. The spiritualuminescent coating is always emitting the glowing, loving guidance of our Savior. Upon receiving the Holy Ghost to power the metaphorical circuit in our souls, greater light is added to that background of spiritualuminescence, as illustrated in the diagrams of figure 3.2.

If it is the presence of our spirit within our body that powers the spiritualuminescence of the Light of Christ, then this would provide some context for the many experiences that have been recorded when light is seen as going out in someone's eyes when he or she dies. In *The Iliad*, death is described with imagery that relates to a darkness coming over the eyes, imagery like the following: "The shades of death, with fate that no man can withstand, came over his eyes."[16] Departure of the spirit from the body, which is the ultimate signification of death, would extinguish emission from the spiritualuminescence of the Light of Christ and may be what has been discerned by so many.

Let's recap this analogy and hypothesis: We all have the Light of Christ, a portion of which is like a light bulb in our souls. This light bulb has two parts: (1) a coating that is spiritualuminescent, giving off a little light that serves as a person's conscience, and (2) an electroluminescent-like light source that emits light based on how much spiritual energy it receives from the Holy Ghost (analogous to the energy from a battery power-ing light emission from a light bulb). When the gift of the Holy Ghost is obtained, we have within us access to the complete source of spiritual energy to bring the Light of Christ to its full brightness in our soul; thus making us like God, who *is* light (see 1 John 1:5). Once the Holy Ghost is with us and powering radiation from the Light of Christ, the only thing keeping us from turning into our own spiritual spotlight is our "natural man" (Mosiah 3:19), which causes resistance to God (analogous to the resistor in the light bulb circuit). We need more faith, obedience, submis-siveness, and, most succinctly, we need to have our "eye single to [God's] glory" (Doctrine and Covenants 88:67). Drawing closer to God reduces our resistance to the Holy Ghost and increases the brightness of the Light of Christ radiating from within us.

Hypothesis 2: Reaction to God's light

The purpose of the thorough analysis in the previous section was, above all, to stir thoughts about how our radiation of spiritual light may work. As noted, the analogy of the light bulb circuit was one hypothesis. To be true to sound scientific inquiry and study, it is worth noting one other hypoth-esis for how the Light of Christ and the Holy Ghost may be related to our spiritual light radiation. This hypothesis focuses on the following doctrine about the Light of Christ: "Which light *proceedeth forth from the presence of God to fill the immensity of space*—the light which is in all things, which giveth life to all things, which is the law by which all things are governed, even the power of God who sitteth upon his throne, who is in the bosom of eternity, who is in the midst of all things" (Doctrine and Covenants 88:12–13; emphasis added).

Imagine all of God's light being sent forth from where he dwells on Kolob (see Abraham 3:3), effectively from the center of the universe. This light must be filtered in some way, perhaps through the veil, since we cannot withstand its full glory in our mortal state. How is this light, which radiates from a central source, kept from being blocked as the earth rotates (which would leave us shadowed for some portion of each day)? Let us assume that the light is able to pass through all physical matter, even matter as thick as the earth. However, this lack of direct line-of-sight access to the source is one of the weaknesses in this hypothesis.

Since this light, the Light of Christ, would be shining upon all people equally, what determines our own radiation of spiritual light? In this hypothesis, I suggest that it is our righteousness and corresponding closeness to the Holy Ghost that determines our radiation of spiritual light. As we more fully yield our will to God's will, the influence of (and our connection to) the Holy Ghost increases. One possible effect of the Holy Ghost's influence is a purification of the interaction between our spirit and body in a way that allows us to be more in tune with the Light of Christ (which is not unlike tuning a radio antenna to pick up a specific station). The Holy Ghost may purify this connection in a transformative way that enhances our interaction with God's light. The baptism "by fire" (Doctrine and Covenants 19:31) may metaphorically weld our spirit and body together in a special manner. Perhaps the result is simply that we then reflect some portion of the incident Light of Christ. Perhaps it is even more than reflection, such as a type of photoluminescence, where the Light of Christ interacts with our spirit/body in a way that generates a distinct type of spiritual light radiating from us. Either way, the increase in our yielding to the Holy Ghost results in a corresponding increase in our radiation of spiritual light that is sourced by the Light of Christ.

In summary, this hypothesis begins with the Light of Christ emanating from a central source and shining on all of us in equal measure. Our radiation of spiritual light is determined by our interaction with the Light of Christ in this sequence: we increase in righteousness → strengthen our connection to the Holy Ghost → make a more purified bonding of the spirit with the body → and enhance the reflection of (or luminescence from) our interaction with the Light of Christ.

Two Distinct Hypotheses

Having now reviewed two hypotheses regarding how the Light of Christ and the Holy Ghost may work in our radiation of spiritual light, let's take a moment to compare them. Juxtaposing the most prominent aspects of the two hypotheses reveals a few key distinctions (see table 3.1). The first hypothesis interprets the Holy Ghost as being an energy source for generating the spiritual light that radiates from the Light of Christ within us, whereas the second hypothesis emphasizes the propagation of the Light of Christ from a centralized, universal source that all people are exposed to and that all people react to based on having the Holy Ghost with them. Other dramatic distinctions can be seen in table 3.1, with the net result being that these two hypotheses are quite different. Most likely, this means the true doctrine is some amalgamation of the two, undoubtedly with further details we are not yet aware of.

Table 3.1. Comparison of the two hypotheses regarding the role of the Light of Christ and the Holy Ghost in our radiation of spiritual light.

	Hypothesis 1: Spiritual Energy	Hypothesis 2: Reaction to God's Light
Role of Light of Christ	The Light of Christ generates spiritual light within every person.	The Light of Christ proceeds from a central location (Kolob) and shines on every person equally.
Role of Holy Ghost	The Holy Ghost provides spiritual energy that fuels the generation of spiritual light.	The Holy Ghost purifies the bond between spirit and body and enhances its interaction with the Light of Christ.

How we radiate spiritual light	Spiritual energy from the Holy Ghost leads to radiation from the Light of Christ within us.	The Light of Christ is reflected, or causes luminescence (i.e., is transformed into spiritual light), from our spirit/body.
Effect of our righteousness	Our righteousness reduces our resistance to the spiritual energy from the Holy Ghost; thus, we radiate more spiritual light.	Our righteousness strengthens our connection to and purification from the Holy Ghost; thus, we radiate more spiritual light.

Coming full circle to the disclaimer provided at the beginning of these hypotheses, I reiterate that they are not doctrine. While true doctrinal principles are used to develop and support the hypotheses, we lack sufficient revealed truths to produce a definitive picture. I hope that the presentation of these perspectives will inspire the reader to ponder on this topic further. The most important truth, consistent in both hypotheses, is that as we increase in righteousness, we radiate more spiritual light.

Holy Ghost versus Light of Christ

To close this discussion of the roles of the Light of Christ and the Holy Ghost in our radiation of spiritual light, I want to reiterate the difficulty that can arise in deciphering between them.[17] One thing is certain: the Light of Christ and the Holy Ghost are *not* the same. One is a divine power that fills the immensity of space, is given to every person, and is the very power by which the sun was made. The other is a member of the Godhead and a personage of spirit. The fact that they can be confused is evidence to me that they must be intricately related in their influence upon us. Let me conclude this discussion by offering a table I have created to compare the titles, attributes, and purposes of the Light of Christ and the Holy Ghost in order to aid the reader in pondering all of this further (see table 3.2).

Table 3.2. Comparison of the titles, attributes, and purposes of the Light of Christ and the Holy Ghost. **Boldface** words indicate similarities, words in *italics* denote opposites, and words in roman font designate unique meanings.

	Light of Christ		Holy Ghost	
Titles	Light of Christ	Alma 28:14; Moroni 7:18; *D&C 88:7	Holy Ghost	3 Nephi 28:11
	Spirit of Christ	Moroni 7:16; 1 Peter 1:11	Spirit of truth	John 16:13
	Spirit of the Lord	1 Nephi 13:15	**Spirit of the Lord**	Ether 12:2; Mosiah 4:3
	Spirit of God	Romans 8:9, 14	**Spirit of God**	Alma 5:47; Moses 6:65
	Light of Life	John 1:4; 8:12	Spirit	1 Nephi 4:6
	Truth	D&C 84:45; 88:7	Spirit of revelation	D&C 8:2-3
	Knowledge	D&C 94:24, 28	Comforter	John 14:26; D&C 42:17
			Holy Spirit	Alma 5:46; D&C 55:3
			Holy Spirit of promise	D&C 132:7; 76:53
Attributes	*Not a personage*	Bible Dictionary (BD), "Light of Christ"	*Personage of spirit*	D&C 130:22
	Fills immensity of space	D&C 88:12	Third member of the Godhead	1 John 5:7; D&C 20:28
	Given to every person	D&C 84:46; 93:2; John 1:9	*Will not always strive with us*	Ether 2:15; 2 Nephi 26:11
	Light of sun & power by which it was made	D&C 88:7-10	*"Gift of" must be given by laying on of hands*	Acts 8:12-25; Moroni 2
	Gives life to all things	D&C 88:13	Knows all things	D&C 35:19
	Law governing all things	D&C 88:13	Speaks to mind & heart	D&C 8:2-3
	Power of God	D&C 88:13		

	Light of Christ		Holy Ghost	
Purpose for us	Conscience; helps know good from evil	Moroni 7:16, 18; D&C 50:24; Isaiah 2:5	Shows all things you should do	2 Nephi 32:5
	Brings joy, uplifts, ennobles, enlightens	BD, "Light of Christ"; Alma 19:6	Brings joy, peace, comfort, longsuffering	Galatians 5:22–23; Alma 17:10; John 14:27
	Leads to find true gospel	D&C 84:46-48; Alma 26:3, 14-15; John 12:46	Guides to, teaches, reveals, and confirms all truth	John 16:13; Moroni 10:5; John 14:26
	Quickens understanding	D&C 88:11, 41	Bears witness of Father and Son	3 Nephi 28:11; Ether 12:41; D&C 42:17
	Gives spiritual gifts	Moroni 10:17	Sanctifies repentant	3 Nephi 27:20; John 3:5
			Seals all covenants	D&C 132:7
			Gives revelation	D&C 68:4; 2 Peter 1:21

*D&C = Doctrine and Covenants

Along with the above table, I also include here, for further consideration, a few of the most prominent quotations from Church leaders regarding the distinction between the Light of Christ and the Holy Ghost. In addition, the most comprehensive of commentaries that I came across in my studies is found in the June 1989 *Ensign* in an "I Have a Question" answer from Brent Bulloch.[18] Keep in mind the two distinct hypotheses presented in this chapter as you study these teachings:

There is a spirit—the Spirit of the Lord, the Spirit of Christ, the light of truth, the light of Christ—that defies description and is beyond mortal comprehension. It is in us and in all things; it is around us and around all things; it fills the earth and the heavens and the universe. It is everywhere, in all immensity, without exception; it is an indwelling, immanent, ever-present, never-absent spirit. It has neither shape nor form nor personality. It is not an entity nor a person nor a personage. It has no agency, does not act independently, and exists not to act but to be acted upon.[19]

The Holy Ghost should not be confused with the Spirit [the light of Christ] which fills the immensity of space and which is everywhere present. This other Spirit is impersonal and has no size, nor dimension; it proceeds forth from the presence of the Father and the Son and is in all things. We should speak of the Holy Ghost as a personage as "he" and this other Spirit as "it," although when we speak of the power or gift of the Holy Ghost we may properly say "it."[20]

The Holy Ghost makes use of the Light of Christ to perform his work. "The Spirit of Christ (or Light of Christ) is the agency through which the Holy Ghost operates," Elder [Bruce R.] McConkie explained. Moroni wrote that all spiritual gifts come through the Spirit of Christ, meaning that when the Holy Ghost works with us, he transmits his gifts by the agency of the light of Christ.

After we are baptized and confirmed and we receive the gift of the Holy Ghost, we may enjoy the gifts of the Holy Ghost through the Holy Ghost's ministration. Since the Holy Ghost uses the Spirit of Christ or Light of Christ to minister to the Saints of God, the term "Spirit of Christ" is sometimes used to refer to the Holy Ghost's ministration through that Spirit.[21]

When it becomes necessary [for the Holy Ghost] to speak to us, he is able to do so by acting through the other Spirit, that is, through the Light of Christ.[22]

[The Holy Ghost influences people] through the increased rays of that light which lighteth every [person] that cometh into the world.[23]

[The gift of the Holy Ghost] is a greater and higher endowment of the same spirit which enlightens every [person] that comes into the world.[24]

There are three phases of the light of Christ that I want to mention. The first one is the light which enlighteneth every [person] that cometh into the world; the second phase is the gift of the Holy Ghost; and the third is the more sure word of prophecy.[25]

While there is still much we do not know about the nature of the Light of Christ and the Holy Ghost, the teachings quoted above provide some insight into their distinctions and interworkings. However, we do know one thing for certain: both are given to bless and aid humankind in our journey to live with God again, and yielding to their influence will make us more like our Eternal Father (see James 1:17; Doctrine and Covenants 50:24; 93:28).

Let Your Light Shine

Everyone radiates spiritual light of some form, intensity, and type. While the Light of Christ is in the world, which results in light radiating from our souls, information from that radiated light will be detectable by others. Considering the unstoppable constancy of our radiation, we can see added meaning in the Savior's injunction to "let [our] light so shine before men" (Matthew 5:16). Examine the counsel of the Savior in its entirety: "Ye are the light of the world. A city that is set on an hill cannot be hid. Neither do men light a candle, and put it under a bushel, but on a candlestick; and it giveth light unto all that are in the house. Let your light so shine before men, that they may see your good works, and glorify your Father which is in heaven" (Matthew 5:14–16).

This commandment is not just about increasing our radiation of spiritual light but also knowing that we must actively allow that light to shine unto others. As was discussed in chapter 2, a key attribute of light is that it travels in a specific direction (think about a flashlight). I think it is safe to assume that the spiritual light radiating from within us is also directional, in its own way. As such, we must focus our spiritual light so that it will shine unto others, thus maximizing the effect of our light in the same way we would focus a flashlight onto the path ahead of a fellow traveler when walking with them in a dark forest.

All forms of physically measurable light have their barriers—such as lead—that will stop the light completely in its path. Likewise, there are barriers to spiritual light (bushels, if you will) that must be avoided in order for our light to shine unto others. To some degree, these bushels can be obvious, like sin or apathy for spiritual things. Some may be a little less obvious, like repeatedly turning down opportunities to serve others, allowing fear to overcome faith, or not sharing the gospel. These examples are all proverbial bushels that smother or block the reach of radiated spiritual light. Think of the parable of the talents in terms of what the Lord used to measure the faithfulness of his servants. It was not enough that a servant had preserved the initial talent or talents (spiritual light) given to every servant, but that those talents were used to generate more talents (letting light shine unto others) (see Matthew 25:14–30).

Returning to the Savior's admonition in Matthew 5, we learn that having our light shine results in others being able to "*see* [our] good works, and glorify [our] Father which is in heaven" (Matthew 5:16; emphasis added). I hope we have come far enough in our discussion about light for you to appreciate that light, which is truth (see Doctrine and Covenants 84:45), can be seen in ways other than with natural eyes. Serving a mission, magnifying a calling, being a faithful ministering brother or sister, and providing service of any type are just a few examples of the ways that we let our light shine unto others.

To close this discussion on the radiation of spiritual light and our responsibility to let this light shine, ponder this excerpt of a general conference address from President Thomas S. Monson:

> As we follow the example of the Savior and live as He lived and as He taught, that light will burn within us and will light the way for others. . . .
>
> As we prove to be examples in word, in conversation, in charity, in spirit, in faith, and in purity, we will qualify to be lights to the world. . . .
>
> My brothers and sisters, our opportunities to shine surround us each day, in whatever circumstance we find ourselves. As we follow the example of the Savior, ours will be the opportunity to be a light in the lives of others, whether they be our family members and friends, co-workers, mere acquaintances, or total strangers.
>
> To each of you, I say that you are a son or daughter of our Heavenly Father. You have come from His presence to live on this earth for a season, to reflect the Savior's love and teachings, and to bravely let your light shine for all to see.[26]

May we follow the counsel of the Master to let our light shine so that others may receive and benefit from the spiritual light we radiate—light that will allow them to feel the Savior's love.

Notes

1. David O. McKay, "Radiation of the Gospel," in Conference Report, April 1963, 129.

2. This is a simplification since there are other processes that may determine the color of an object. For instance, an object could absorb all of the light that hits it and then, via photoluminescence, emit new photons that are of a certain wavelength (e.g., visible red).

3. Parley P. Pratt, *Key to the Science of Theology* (London: F. D. Richards, 1855), 38–41.

4. McKay, "Radiation of the Gospel," 129.

5. "Talk by President David O. McKay Given to the North British Mission 1 March 1961," Family and Church History Department Archives, The Church of Jesus Christ of Latter-day Saints, 3.

6. Thomas Carlyle, *On Heroes, Hero-Worship, and the Heroic in History*, ed. Archibald MacMechan (Boston: Ginn, 1901), 2.

7. Gordon B. Hinckley, "'God Hath Not Given Us the Spirit of Fear,'" *Ensign*, October 1984, 1.

8. Dieter F. Uchtdorf, "Bearers of Heavenly Light," *Ensign*, November 2017, 79.

9. Uchtdorf, "Bearers of Heavenly Light," 80.

10. Robert D. Hales, "Out of Darkness into His Marvelous Light," *Ensign*, May 2002, 70–71.

11. The Bible Dictionary under the heading for "Light of Christ" explains, "Biblical phrases that are sometimes synonymous to the term 'light of Christ' are 'spirit of the Lord' and 'light of life' (see, for example, John 1:4; 8:12). The *'spirit of the Lord,'* however, sometimes is used with reference to the Holy Ghost and so must not be taken in every case as referring to the light of Christ."

12. Elder Parley P. Pratt taught, "The gift of the Holy Spirit . . . quickens all the intellectual faculties, increases, enlarges, expands, and purifies all the natural passions and affections; and adapts them, by the gift of wisdom, to their lawful use. . . . In short, it is, as it were . . . joy to the heart [and] light to the eyes." Pratt, *Key to the Science of Theology*, 98–99.

13. Daniel K Judd, "The Spirit of Christ: A Light amid Darkness," *Liahona*, May 2001, 19; emphasis added.

14. Marion G. Romney, "The Light of Christ," *Ensign*, May 1977, 44.

15. Brigham Young, in *Journal of Discourses* (London: Latter-day Saints' Book Depot, 1881), 6:315.

16. Homer, *Iliad* 5.48–58.

17. A useful perspective on the Light of Christ—including some useful quotes, references, and discussion on how the Light of Christ compares to the Holy Ghost—is available at David Snell, "Here's Everything We Know about the Light of Christ (and It's Pretty Darn Cool)," *Third Hour*, 14 September 2017, https://thirdhour.org/blog/faith/gospel-doctrine/light-of-christ.

18. Brent Bulloch, "I Have a Question: The Holy Ghost, the Spirit of Christ, and the Light of Christ," *Ensign*, June 1989, 26–28.

19. Bruce R. McConkie, *A New Witness for the Articles of Faith* (Salt Lake City: Deseret Book, 1985), 257.

20. Joseph Fielding Smith, *Doctrines of Salvation* (Salt Lake City: Bookcraft, 1954–56), 1:49–50.

21. Bulloch, "The Holy Ghost," 26.

22. Smith, *Doctrines of Salvation*, 1:41.

23. Young, in *Journal of Discourses*, 6:315.

24. Charles W. Penrose, in *Journal of Discourses*, 23:350.

25. Romney, "Light of Christ," 43.

26. Thomas S. Monson, "Be an Example and a Light," *Ensign*, November 2015, 87–88.

4

Sensing Light with Our Spirits

Faith emits a spiritual light, and that light is discernible.[1]

—Elder Neil L. Andersen

Sometime in November 1895, as the chill of fall was gripping the town of Würzburg, Germany, there was a scientist who hadn't left his laboratory in weeks. Wilhelm Röntgen, a professor at the University of Würzburg, had become so consumed by the thrill of his recent experiments that he had been eating and sleeping in the lab. His astonishment grew with each day as he studied what he believed to be a new type of radiation. Fittingly, it was a faint glimmer of light coming from a fluorescent screen in the corner of his lab that had led Röntgen to feverishly explore the possibility of these "new kind[s] of rays."[2]

At one point, Röntgen convinced his wife, Bertha, to assist him; perhaps she was roped in unwittingly while checking whether he was still alive! He had Bertha hold her hand in the path of his newly discovered rays while he held a photographic plate behind her hand. He then developed the plate, which became the very first "röntgenogram." The generated image not only showed the delicate skeletal structure of Bertha's hand, but clearly displayed a metal ring she was wearing as well. It so terrified her to see her own skeleton that Bertha exclaimed, "I have seen my death!" Thrilled with this discovery, yet still uncertain what these rays were, Röntgen dubbed them X-rays, using the mathematical term X to denote something unknown. Despite the considerable fame and fortune he could have pursued from his discovery, Röntgen elected not to patent or otherwise inhibit others from using the rays, in favor of enabling widespread invention and opportunities. Röntgen is now considered the father of diagnostic radiology.

Shortly after Röntgen's experiments were published, it was discovered that his X-rays were nothing more than electromagnetic radiation of higher energy than visible light. Certain materials were shown to be more capable of stopping the X-rays (such as lead or bone) while others proved uniquely sensitive to them and thus suitable for capturing images. What was landmark about Röntgen's discovery was not just that he had revealed a new type of radiation but that he had shown how useful information could be obtained by the proper detection of the ray. Six years after his initial experiments, Röntgen became the inaugural recipient of the Nobel Prize in Physics in 1901.

Radiation Detection

The electromagnetic radiation that we are exposed to in the dentist's chair or at the radiologist's office is of sufficiently high energy as to pass through most things, including the body. However, it won't pass through certain things. For instance, calcium will absorb high-energy radiation. Since bone has a high concentration of calcium, this provides a contrast between the areas with and without bone in the path of a beam of X-rays. While they cannot be felt under the low-dose exposures used for medical imaging, X-rays do have an impact on the body. This is why X-ray technicians leave the room or stand behind specially insulated walls or lead shields when taking images. While the physical senses of our bodies may not detect the X-rays, special photographic or digital plates *are* able to detect the number of X-rays that hit them, thus creating an image of the exposed area (which is brighter where X-rays are blocked by bone).

Beyond medical X-rays, we are constantly exposed to various types of electromagnetic radiation that also cannot be felt. Virtually all such radiation is too low in energy and intensity (the number of photons) to do any harm: radio waves, communication waves (emitted and received by cell phones), microwaves, wireless internet data waves, and so forth. These are all known as *nonionizing* forms of radiation, which can be thought of as *almost* harmless. Most nonionizing radiation will pass right through your body. A small amount will be absorbed, causing your body to heat up, but not enough to disrupt the atomic structure of the cells. With high enough concentration or intensity—meaning a large number of photons—these nonionizing light waves can transfer a significant amount of energy to something; just think of a microwave oven, which is able to heat items by exposing them to microwave radiation.

What kind of radiation *does* disrupt the atomic structure of cells? That would be considered *ionizing radiation*. All high-energy waves have the potential to be ionizing, including ultraviolet rays, X-rays, and gamma rays. These are the ones we have to limit our exposure to because the ionization of the atoms that make up our bodies can lead to cancer—a multiplication of deformed molecules or cells in the body.[3]

So, we have electromagnetic radiation (dubbed "light," whether visible or not, in this book) that can vary from low to high energy. We also know that this electromagnetic radiation is used for technology like X-rays because it characteristically travels through certain things and not others. The next question is, What determines whether the light will pass through or be absorbed by the object or person in its path? To answer this, both the properties of the light *and* the atomic and physical structure of the object (including a person's body) must be considered.

As mentioned above, high-energy (ionizing) light is potentially dangerous; however, most of this light will pass right through the human body (which, physically, is predominantly water). Conversely, a solid plate of lead will absorb all of the light. The lead is not thicker than the body, but it has an atomic structure (the size and configuration of its atoms) that causes it to be absorptive. Similar to high-energy light, low-energy light (such as radio waves) will also pass through the body, as well as most other objects (even buildings). There are some things that can absorb both the low- and high-energy light, such as mountains. You've probably noticed that you tend to lose your radio signal while driving in mountainous areas. This is because mountains are much thicker and denser than buildings and are thus able to absorb even low-energy light waves.

I know this may seem counterintuitive: light with low energy is able to pass through objects in a fashion similar to light with high energy. But, remember that *all light is moving at the same speed*. The energy does make a difference, but primarily because it is related to the wavelength of the light waves. Basically, if the wavelength of a photon of light is very small (high-energy light) or very large (low-energy light), then it has a high probability of passing through an object. But when the wavelength is in the midrange, meaning it is similar in size to the size/spacing of molecules that make up an object, then the light has a higher chance of being absorbed or reflected rather than being transmitted straight through.

Hence, it is the light of midrange energy (such as visible light) that we have *physically* noticeable interactions with. For instance, you don't really expect that a flashlight pointed at a wall will shine light through to the other side, right? Instead, most of the light will just bounce off the wall and scatter around the room, making it a bit brighter. If you now press that flashlight directly against the palm of your hand, you may notice that your hand will look like it is glowing. This happens because the light is bouncing around a bit inside of your hand before it is fully diffused.

Now, despite what you know about how walls can keep visible light in, you would also fully expect your Wi-Fi signal (also light of midrange energy) to readily transmit through a wall (and, thankfully, much of the signal does). Seems confusing, right? Visible light does not seem to make it through the wall but the Wi-Fi signal does; yet they are both forms of light with midrange energy. The point of this discussion is that there are subtleties related to how light interacts with specific objects that cannot be classified generally based only on the energy of the light. What is clear is that, at the very least, the combination of (1) the type of the light (energy/wavelength) and (2) the atomic structure and thickness of the object must be considered jointly when determining how light and objects will interact.

Graphene—the Difference of a Single Layer of Atoms

Let's specifically examine the role that thickness of a material plays in determining the interaction with light. Our previous example of radio waves showed that while they may make it through buildings, they don't have the same success with mountains. This begs the question of how thick a material needs to be in order to make a detectable difference in the absorption or reflection of light. As we are soon going to delve into a discussion of how our spirits may detect light, it is important to understand what is known about this topic through recent scientific experiments with atomically small (thin) materials. Allow me to introduce you to the world's thinnest known material: graphene. We will see how even a material that is only one atomic layer in thickness, when placed on a particular substrate (surface supporting the graphene), is able to cause detectable interactions with light.

Graphene is a single layer of carbon atoms arranged in a honeycomb fashion (like chicken wire), as depicted in figure 4.1. It is called a two-dimensional (2D) material because it has no attachments (bonds) to other materials above or below it; it has only in-plane bonds. You are definitely familiar with the material graphite since you've no doubt used a pencil. The

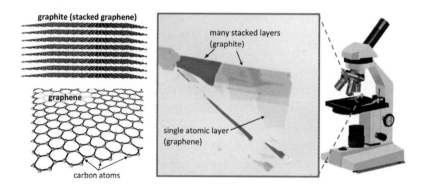

Figure 4.1. Schematic representation of graphene, which is a single sheet of carbon atoms arranged (bound together) in a honeycomb structure. When many layers of graphene are stacked together, they form graphite. The microscope image in the middle shows that, when placed on an appropriate substrate, even a single layer of atoms (graphene) is made visible, though it is fainter than the thicker (graphite) layers. (See spiritualphysicsoflight.com.)

reason it's prominently used in pencils is because of the ease with which graphite flakes off when rubbed. Graph*ite* is simply many, many layers of graph*ene* all stacked together. Since the mid-2000s, graphene has caught the attention of the scientific world because of its unique, record-breaking properties. This includes, but is not limited to, its impressive mechanical strength and superb ability to conduct electricity. The 2010 Nobel Prize in Physics was awarded to two researchers who were able to successfully isolate a single atomic layer of graphene and study its properties.[4]

Entire books have been written about the properties of graphene, but our interest in it is focused on just one attribute: how this atomically thin material *is* and *is not* able to be detected by its interactions with light. First, let's discuss how graphene is *not* detectable. If you were able to grab a sheet of graphene the size of a piece of notebook paper and hold it up, you would *not* be able to see it or feel it. The graphene is so thin that virtually all light will pass right through it without being disrupted; hence, the graphene would be invisible. In terms of feeling the graphene between your fingers, consider that a single cell in the human body is made up of about 20 trillion atoms (that's 20×10^{14}) and that an average adult contains about 100 trillion cells (10^{13}). Pressing a sheet of carbon atoms that is one atomic layer thick between your fingers is not going to be noticeable because the sheet is hardly able to interact with the comparably enormous number (billions) of cells in your fingertips.

How then is graphene identified? It turns out that if this invisible single atomic layer of material is placed onto a glass-like substrate (silicon dioxide), it can be readily detected by the naked eye (provided the size, or area, of the piece of graphene is large enough to be seen). If the size of the piece of graphene is small, then a standard optical microscope can be used to readily see it on the glass-like substrate (as shown in figure 4.1). A million-dollar electron microscope or extremely advanced and specialized imaging technique wouldn't be necessary—just the most standard piece of scientific equipment available. What makes the graphene visible is how it disrupts the light hitting the glass-like surface, which causes the light to be reflected and absorbed differently. Remember, the hypothetical sheet of graphene you are holding between your fingertips would be completely invisible. Yet, when applied to a particular substrate, the graphene causes sufficient disruption of the light so as to make a visible change. Imagine, just a single layer of atoms being able to cause such a noticeable difference! You can see an example of this in figure 4.1, where a single layer of graphene is compared to some thicker layers (multiple layers of graphene stacked on top of each other to form graphite).

Before transitioning to how these scientific principles and observations contribute to our understanding of the sensing of spiritual light, let's summarize: Electromagnetic radiation, or light, can range from low to high energy. At either extreme, the radiation will pass through most objects except for those that are very thick (especially for low-energy light) or have a unique atomic structure for absorbing the light, such as lead or calcium. The rest of the light will be absorbed or reflected by objects, including our bodies, depending on their atomic structures. Thickness of a material or object does matter—the thinner, the easier to pass through—but so does the atomic structure *and* the interaction of the material with its surroundings.

Spiritual Matter

Experiments on graphene show how even the thinnest known material, a single sheet of carbon atoms, can have significant and detectable interactions with light based on what that material is placed on. Now we will turn our attention to how this all relates to spiritual matter and the sensing of spiritual light. As mentioned earlier, our spirits have physical substance to them: "There is no such thing as immaterial matter. All spirit is matter, but it is more fine or pure, and can only be discerned by purer eyes; We cannot see it; but when our bodies are purified we shall see that it is all matter" (Doctrine and Covenants 131:7–8).

Think about the two different ways our physical bodies are able to detect light. For one, we can actually *feel* the light from the sun as our bodies absorb it. That absorption is a transfer of energy from the sunlight to the atoms in our bodies, causing us to heat up and feel warm. Secondly, our physical eyes are able to *see* visible light, which is radiation within a specific energy range. The energy ranges of light that we absorb (and in some cases actually feel) or are able to see are determined based on physical features: atomic structure, thickness of our body, and so forth.

As mentioned above, think about what happens when you shine a very bright light right up against your fingertip—one of the thinnest parts of your body. A portion of the light will shine through your skin and even bounce around a bit inside, making it appear as if your fingertip is glowing. This happens because of the size and density of your body in that region. Conversely, you'd never expect a light held directly against your stomach to shine through and be visible from behind.

Now think about our spirits. In a way similar to graphene, the "more fine or pure" matter that makes up our spirits renders them invisible to our physical eyes. In other words, visible light passes right through spirits in the same fashion as it does for a sheet of graphene held in the air. But what about when spiritual matter is placed within a physical body? Considering what we know about graphene—when placed on certain substrates it causes a readily detectable interaction with light—it seems appropriate to conclude that *having spiritual matter placed into a physical body will enable unique interactions with certain types of light.* After all, our purpose for being here on Earth and receiving a physical body is to enable us to grow spiritually by passing through certain experiences; why not also learn to use the unique interaction between our spirit (spiritual matter) and body to discern more and more spiritual light? Remember these scriptures:

> For the dead had looked upon the long absence of their spirits from their bodies as a bondage. (Doctrine and Covenants 138:50)

> For as ye have looked upon the long absence of your spirits from your bodies to be a bondage, I will show unto you how the day of redemption shall come, and also the restoration of the scattered Israel. (Doctrine and Covenants 45:17)

I suggest that the bondage these scriptures refer to is, at least in part, related to the unique interactions with light that our spirits are deprived of when they are not being housed in our bodies. It is this unique combination of body and spirit that makes up our souls (see Doctrine and Covenants 88:15).[5] We often learn that we came to earth to obtain physical bodies, and this truth becomes all the more meaningful when we realize that without these bodies, we likely could not detect (or ultimately, discern) the spiritual light that is needed for our eternal growth.

While we cannot model the precise interaction that happens between spiritual matter and the physical body, it is clear that the spirit is more capable and more powerful with the body, while the spirit is ultimately in a state of bondage without the body. When we are resurrected, each of our spirits will be brought together with a more glorified body. It is interesting to note that there will be a distinct difference between the *bodies* that are telestial, terrestrial, and celestial:

> There are also celestial bodies, and bodies terrestrial: but the glory of the celestial is one, and the glory of the terrestrial is another. (1 Corinthians 15:40)

> These are they whose bodies are celestial, whose glory is that of the sun, even the glory of God, the highest of all, whose glory the sun of the firmament is written of as being typical. . . . Wherefore, they are bodies terrestrial, and not bodies celestial, and differ in glory as the moon differs from the sun. (Doctrine and Covenants 76:70, 78)

Reflect also on what President Joseph Fielding Smith taught on this topic:

> In the resurrection there will be different kinds of bodies; they will not all be alike. The body [one] receives will determine [one's] place hereafter. There will be celestial bodies, terrestrial bodies, and telestial bodies, and these bodies will differ as distinctly as do bodies here. . . . Some will gain celestial bodies with all the powers of exaltation and eternal increase. These bodies will shine like the sun as our Savior's does, as described by John. Those who enter the terrestrial kingdom will have terrestrial bodies, and they will not shine like the sun, but they will be more glorious than the bodies of those who receive the telestial glory.[6]

Nothing is mentioned about the difference in the *spiritual* matter of resurrected beings. In fact, Amulek taught that the "same spirit which doth possess your bodies at the time that ye go out of this life . . . will have power to possess your body in that eternal world" (Alma 34:34). This isn't to suggest that there isn't growth and development that occurs for spirits; there very well will be (see Doctrine and Covenants 136). We are also aware that such progression happened during our first estate, in the premortal realm (e.g., see Abraham 3:22–25). It seems, however, that the creation of the soul, when body and spirit join, is a union that significantly amplifies the ability of an individual to grow in spiritual light beyond what a spirit on its own ever could. The greater refinement of a celestial body compared to a terrestrial body must be related to light, since the celestial body has glory like the sun, even like the glory of Christ. Perhaps it is that the celestial body provides the perfect substrate for the spirit to be connected to so that it radiates *and* detects all spiritual light.

Sensing Spiritual Light

Now that we have explored how spiritual matter—when combined with bodies to create souls—may enable more profound interactions with spiritual light, let us consider what it means to sense or detect spiritual light. To set the stage for the present discussion, I will return to a quote from President David O. McKay cited earlier in the book:

> Every person is a recipient of radiation. The Savior was conscious of that. Whenever he came into the presence of an individual, he sensed that radiation—whether it was the woman of Samaria with her past life; whether it was the woman who was to be stoned or the men who were to stone her; whether it was the statesman, Nicodemus, or one of the lepers. He was conscious of the radiation from the individual. And to a degree so are you, and so am I. It is what we are and what we radiate that affects the people around us.[7]

As indicated in President McKay's statement, numerous examples could be given of how the Savior detected the radiation of spiritual light from individuals around him. It was not exclusive to the detection of the strong emission of spiritual light from righteous individuals; rather, it involved the detection of radiation from everyone, including those who were troubled, sad, or deep in sin.

The Savior's example tells us something fascinating about the sensing of spiritual light: the soul is capable of determining so much more than just the magnitude or intensity of the light. To illustrate this, recall what we are able to detect about visible light with our natural eyes. First, and most prominently, we can detect the intensity of visible light. It is very clear to us when something is visibly bright (like a flashlight in our eyes) or when something is dark (like a moonless night). Second, we are able to detect the energy (or wavelength) of visible light. You may have never thought about it like this, but the reason we see color is because the optic nerve and brain are translating different wavelengths of light into certain hues of color. This is the extent of information we receive about the light that we see—its intensity and wavelength/color. Our brains are constantly receiving this information from light and translating it into useful information that helps us navigate the world around us.

Now think about the type of information the soul is able to interpret from the radiation of spiritual light coming from others. Just as we can *feel* and *see* some forms of light with our physical bodies, our souls seem to have similar capabilities. There are times when a person's emotional pain is clearly perceivable, whether that person is depressed, upset, or concerned. There are powerful feelings of peace, reassurance, and comfort that we feel coming from certain individuals just by being near them. It could be said that some of these feelings are deduced from the words or actions of—or from previous interactions with—the individual; yet, there are times when these feelings are discerned by nothing more than a person's presence. Further, there are occasions when the lack of spiritual light from an individual is so palpable that feelings of discomfort will be generated in those around them. These feelings might alert one to escape from a potentially dangerous situation.[8]

There are also instances when a surge of spiritual light is detected in a very distinct and memorable fashion through spiritual sight. There are countless conversion stories that begin with a person noticing something different about the missionaries that caught their attention. These first encounters with the missionaries are often described with a phrase like, "they seemed to glow." There are also times when a member of the Church is picked out from a crowd because someone "could just tell" they were members.

When my family lived in New York, the closest temple was in New York City. My wife and I enjoyed playing a little game whenever we went to the temple together. As we walked toward the temple from an off-site parking garage, we loved to find those in the crowd who were also on their way to the Lord's house. Despite the sea of well-dressed men and women carrying small bags or briefcases on the bustling streets, it was clear who was headed to the temple and who was headed to the office. There seemed to be an unmistakable glow that caught our spiritual eyes. President Thomas S. Monson related the following story about the distinctive detection of spiritual light:

> To illustrate that the light which comes from a pure and loving spirit is recognized by others, I share with you an experience of many years ago.
>
> At that time, leaders of the Church met with officials in Jerusalem to work out a lease agreement for land on which the Church's Jerusalem Center would be built. In order to obtain the permissions needed, the Church had to agree that no proselyting would be undertaken by our members who would occupy the center. After that agreement had been made, one of the Israeli officials, who was well acquainted with the Church and its members, remarked that he knew the Church would honor the no-proselyting agreement. "But," he said, referring to the students who would attend there, "what are we going to do about the light that is in their eyes?" May that special light ever shine within us, that it might be recognized and appreciated by others.[9]

Another example occurred during the translation of the Book of Mormon by Joseph Smith and Oliver Cowdery in the Whitmer home in Fayette, New York. Here is the account from the Church's history website: "Sarah Conrad, a neighbor hired to help Mary Whitmer in her kitchen, also gained a testimony during the translation process. Sarah had noticed light shining from the faces of Joseph and Oliver as they came downstairs. When she learned from her employer that the change in the men's countenances was 'connected with a holy sacred work,' she believed and later joined the new church."[10]

One other example that I really enjoy was related by President James E. Faust about a student nurse named Constance. She was assigned to help a woman who had been seriously injured but who was refusing to come to the hospital for medical attention. Constance's righteous example became transformative for the woman, who eventually agreed to receive the needed medical aid:

When Constance visited her, the woman smiled as she said, "You convinced me." Then, quite unexpectedly, she asked Constance, "What church do you belong to?" Constance told her she was a member of The Church of Jesus Christ of Latter-day Saints. The woman said: "I knew it. I knew you were sent to me from the first day that I saw you. There was a light in your face that I had noticed in others of your faith. I had to put my trust in you." . . . The missionaries met with her, and she was baptized soon after. All of this because she noticed the light in that young student nurse's face.[11]

Volumes could be filled with similar examples. I'm sure you are now thinking of your own experiences when the distinct presence of your light or someone else's was deeply influential to you or someone you know. There have actually been attempts to scientifically study this glow coming from members of The Church of Jesus Christ of Latter-day Saints, with results showing a subtle, though statistically significant, propensity for members to be correctly identified.[12] Because the primary mechanism for detecting light is the soul, it is certainly not limited to members of the Church. In fact, as mentioned above, it is often the sensing of spiritual light that first brings one to seek a witness of gospel truths.

It is important to note that the above is not meant to suggest that members of the Church have a monopoly on radiating goodness via spiritual light. Any good, moral person will radiate their goodness as they are influenced by the Light of Christ. As Elder D. Todd Christofferson taught, "Those who profess no religious belief can be, and often are, good, moral people. . . . This [does not] happen without divine influence. I am referring to the Light of Christ."[13] There does not need to be recognition of the source of radiated spiritual light in order for the light to be radiated—it is an unconscious influence defined only by who we are. That said, the more individuals learn truth and choose to believe and obey that truth, the more light they will radiate that is associated with that truth.

As for further, specific information that may be gleaned from the spiritual light we detect (beyond the fact that it is good), we will discuss this in detail in chapter 5. It turns out that there is a great deal of information that may be transmitted; in fact, it's quite clear that the limits are far beyond our comprehension. In one specific example, the spiritual light radiation that accompanies the bearing of a sincere testimony can be laced with remarkably deep and powerful truths even when coming from a person of limited experience, such as a child. Once I was leading a discussion in a class at church and wanted to demonstrate the power of testimony that can come from anyone. To show this, I shared a video clip of Elder Bruce R. McConkie bearing his testimony, which was refined, eloquent, and powerful. Then, I had my six-year-old son, Blake, come in and share a talk he had recently given in Primary. Blake's testimony was simple, succinct, *and powerful*. Eternal truths with deep insights and meanings penetrated the hearts of the class members, exemplifying how profound the truths transmitted in spiritual light can surely be—regardless of the simplicity of the words or experiences of the testator. I think all of us in the class that day felt similar to the Nephites during Jesus's ministry among them when "babes did open their mouths and utter marvelous things" (3 Nephi 26:16), "even greater than [Jesus] had revealed unto the people" (26:14). We sensed great truths, even marvelous things, from the radiated spiritual light that accompanied the testimony of a six-year-old.

Our Inescapable Influence on Others

Recognizing the ability of all people to sense spiritual light, we must remember that our radiation of light will be an ever-present influence on others. It's not just what we say or what we do that matters, but *who we are* that influences the world around us. There may be some who do not believe in unseen spiritual influences, yet even they cannot deny the presence of other unseen forces such as magnetism, electricity, gravity, and (of course) light of all energies. The influence from the radiation of a person's spiritual light is just as measurable as these unseen forces of nature, but measurement must happen through the instrumentation of the soul rather than on lab benches or in scientific apparatuses. As President Thomas S. Monson taught:

Each of us came to earth having been given the Light of Christ. . . .

. . . [W]e are to be an example in spirit. To me that means we strive to have in our lives kindness, gratitude, forgiveness, and goodwill. These qualities will provide for us a spirit which will touch the lives of those around us. It has been my opportunity through the years to associate with countless individuals who possess such a spirit. We experience a special feeling when we are with them, a feeling that makes us want to associate with them and to follow their example. They radiate the Light of Christ and help us feel His love for us.[14]

A dearth of spiritual light radiation is also something detectable. Perhaps there has been a time in your life when you have been able to detect a person's spiritual decay by simply being in that person's presence. Or maybe there have been times when you have gleaned other information from the light radiated by those around you. My wife is especially sentient in this way. There have been numerous occasions when we came to learn that what she had detected regarding the sadness, pain, or spiritual decline that someone was experiencing was indeed accurate. Just as our physical temperature (and associated thermal radiation) changes when we are ill, our spiritual temperature and associated spiritual radiation seems also to be affected when we are spiritually unwell for any reason.

In short, all of us are constantly radiating some level of spiritual light from the Light of Christ based on our faith and obedience. Meanwhile, the level of our radiation is continuously influencing those around us, adding meaning to every moment, underscoring every utterance, and accenting every action. The messages encoded within this radiated light are far deeper and more meaningful than many realize (something for further discussion in the next chapter). Elder Carl W. Buehner summarized this concept so succinctly when he said, "They may forget what you said—but they will never forget how you made them feel."[15]

One of the best descriptions of the inescapable and powerful reality of our radiation and its influence on others was described by author William George Jordan. Jordan was not a member of The Church of Jesus Christ of Latter-day Saints but became a friend to Heber J. Grant through years of correspondence that began when President Grant was serving as president of the European Mission in England in the early 1900s. President Grant came upon Jordan's book published in 1902, *The Power of Truth*, and was so impressed by Jordan's discussion of truth that he purchased four thousand copies! Eventually, President Grant, in cooperation with Deseret Book Company, purchased the copyright and printing plates in 1933 from Jordan's widow.[16] Clearly, President Grant felt a deep appreciation for Jordan's ability to describe the meanings and consequences of truth in ways that were in concert with the gospel of Jesus Christ. Jordan's writings are reminiscent of C. S. Lewis's—both are rich in true Christian principles and cherished for how consistently they resonate with gospel teachings.

In the same way that President Grant had a deep appreciation for Jordan's writings on truth, I find Jordan's description of how each individual's radiation influences others to be incredibly profound. He may not use the term *spiritual body radiation* or talk about spiritual light, but based on everything that has been discussed thus far, I think you can appreciate the correlation as you read the following excerpt from Jordan (because this excerpt was written in 1902, masculine nouns and pronouns like *man* and *he* are used to refer generically to people of all genders):

The only responsibility that a man cannot evade in this life is the one he thinks of least,—his personal influence. Man's conscious influence, when he is on dress-parade, when he is posing to impress those around him,—is woefully small. But his unconscious influence, the silent, subtle radiation of his personality, the effect of his words and acts, the trifles he never considers,—is tremendous. Every moment of life he is changing to a degree the life of the whole world. . . .

All the forces of Nature,—heat, light, electricity and gravitation,— are silent and invisible. We never see them; we only know that they exist by seeing the effects they produce. In all Nature the wonders of the "seen" are dwarfed into insignificance when compared with the majesty and glory of the "unseen."

Into the hands of every individual is given a marvellous [*sic*] power for good or for evil,—the silent, unconscious, unseen influence of his life. This is simply the constant radiation of what a man really is, not what he pretends to be. Every man, by his mere living, is radiating sympathy, or sorrow, or morbidness, or cynicism, or happiness, or hope, or any of a hundred other qualities. Life is a state of constant radiation and absorption; to exist is to radiate; to exist is to be the recipient of radiations. . . .

Man cannot escape for one moment from this radiation of his character, this constantly weakening or strengthening of others. He cannot evade the responsibility by saying it is an unconscious influence. He can select the qualities that he will permit to be radiated. He can cultivate sweetness, calmness, trust, generosity, truth, justice, loyalty, nobility,—make them vitally active in his character,—and by these qualities he will constantly affect the world.[17]

It can be both inspiring and perhaps a bit daunting to realize the constant influence we have on those around us.

Looking for Light

The last aspect of sensing spiritual light I'd like to discuss is our need to look for the light radiated by others. One of the most discouraging responses a person can receive when they radiate light is to have it go unnoticed. Many sermons have been preached encouraging us not to care so much about whether someone notices our radiated light ("thy Father which seeth in secret himself shall reward thee openly"; Matthew 6:4). While this type of humility is certainly appropriate, it doesn't change the fact that having our light—including the good we do—acknowledged by others brings us great fulfillment and meaning. I don't think it would hurt for us to try a little harder to see and acknowledge the light radiated from others. Doing so helps to keep us focused on the good in others—fueling their radiation of light rather than allowing the lack thereof to consume what remains of a relationship. This can be especially true of marriage and other family relationships in which we need both radiated light and occasional acknowledgment of our own radiation.

I was reminded of this important principle by my son Grant when he was nine years old. Grant was a rough, tough, play-hard boy—the type of kid that really lives his moments to the fullest; though, at the age of nine, the appropriate boundaries for such a lifestyle were not very well internalized or regarded. In other words, he was doing things that got him into trouble . . . a lot. During a time when Grant had been having a particularly difficult spell with those boundaries, my wife and I talked about him with deep concern. We felt he was severely lacking in positive interactions with us, since he spent most of his time in the thick of something he shouldn't have been doing. I began praying for opportunities to see the good in my son. Around this time, one Monday evening, it was nearing dinnertime and it was Grant's turn to set the cups at the table. The "setting of the cups" at our home somehow evolved into the perfect passive-aggressive opportunity for our kids to get even with each other for any squabbles they'd had that day. To get back at their siblings, the one in charge of setting the cups would simply distribute to each person the cup that was most despised by that person. That night, I was about halfway down the stairs when I realized I had a perfect view of Grant setting the cups. He didn't see me watching him, and no one else was around. He was standing in front of his brother's and sister's places at the table, staring hard at the pink cup he had set at his brother's spot and the blue Spider-Man cup he'd given his sister—cups he knew they hated. As I watched him, I could tell he was really considering his choice. Suddenly, he quickly reached out, picked up the cups, and switched their places—giving each sibling his or her favorite cup—and scurried on his way.

Dinner proceeded normally with no mention of the cups. That night I taught the family home evening lesson. I shared an example of how something my daughter had done recently had really inspired me and brought the Spirit more fully into my life. At the conclusion of my story, Grant, my wild little nine-year old, looked sheepishly at the ground and asked, "Dad, do you have a story like that about me?" I did. In a way I can only describe as heaven-sent, I had been blessed to observe his actions while setting the cups for dinner that very evening. I shared my observation with him and pointed out that his decision brought more light into our home and my life, showing me an example of kindness. He grinned from ear to ear, and my heart filled with love for him. He wanted so very much to be good! But, as with all of us, he needed his light to be noticed—even looked for. As we all actively search for the light in our spouses, children, and family members, it will help us to see them more fully as the Savior sees them.

Just as a single atomic layer of carbon atoms in the form of graphene is able to detect visible light, so is our soul able to sense spiritual light. The impact of such light can be substantial, bringing emotional, intellectual, and spiritual change almost instantaneously. As we draw closer to the Lord, we refine our ability to sense valuable, eternal truths from the spiritual light of others. As we strive to be more sensitive to the light that is constantly influencing us, and as we look for and acknowledge the light we detect from others, the Holy Ghost will magnify our ability to learn from the light. This result will ultimately lead us to discerning more and more light. We must now consider the depth of information that can be embedded within the light we are sensing.

Notes

1. Neil L. Andersen, "Faith Is Not by Chance, but by Choice," *Ensign*, November 2015, 65.

2. H. H. Seliger, "Wilhelm Conrad Röntgen and the Glimmer of Light," *Physics Today*, November 1995, 25–31.

3. Note that the ionization of cells in the body from high-energy radiation (light) is not the sole cause of cancer. In fact, it happens very rarely. The point is that such radiation does have the potential to cause damage to cells, and should those cells multiply, a malignant tumor would develop.

4. The microscope image of graphene shown in figure 4.1 is from a sample created using the same method that led to the Nobel Prize. This method involves placing a small flake of graphite onto a piece of tape, then repeatedly folding and sticking the tape to the graphite flake and retracting it, which causes the flake to be divided into thinner flakes that are spread around on the tape. Repeating this process yields resultant flakes that are thinner and thinner. Finally, the thinned graphite (that has caused the tape to take on a grayish color) is transferred to a glass-like substrate by sticking the tape to the substrate's surface and then peeling it back off. See K. S. Novoselov et al., "Electric Field Effect in Atomically Thin Carbon Films," *Science*, October 2004, 666–69. For a video that demonstrates this process, see https://youtube.com/watch?v=waO020l25sU.

5. Elder James E. Talmage taught, "It is peculiar to the theology of the Latter-day Saints that we regard the body as an essential part of the soul. Read your dictionaries, the lexicons, and encyclopedias, and you will find that nowhere, outside of the Church of Jesus Christ, is the solemn and eternal truth taught that the soul of man is the body and the spirit combined. It is quite the rule to regard the soul as that incorporeal part of men, that immortal part which existed before the body was framed and which shall continue to exist after that body has gone to decay; nevertheless, that is not the soul; that is only a part of the soul; that is the spirit-man, the form in which every individual of us, and every individual human being, existed before [being] called to take tabernacle in the flesh. It has been

declared in the solemn word of revelation, that the spirit and the body constitute the soul of man; and, therefore, we should look upon this body as something that shall endure in the resurrected state, beyond the grave, something to be kept pure and holy." James E. Talmage, in Conference Report, October 1913, 117.

6. Joseph Fielding Smith, *Doctrines of Salvation* (Salt Lake City: Bookcraft, 1954–56), 2:286–87.

7. David O. McKay, "Radiation of the Gospel," in Conference Report, April 1963, 129.

8. These examples of the types of information obtained from sensing spiritual light can also be understood as the presence or absence of the Holy Ghost since there is always a direct correlation between the attendance of spiritual light and the Holy Ghost. As was discussed in the preceding chapter, one possible way of thinking about this connection is that the Holy Ghost is the energy fueling the radiation of spiritual light from the Light of Christ in our souls.

9. Thomas S. Monson, "Be an Example and a Light," *Ensign*, November 2015, 87.

10. Curtis Ashton, "Peter Whitmer Log Home in Fayette, NY," *Historic Sites*, https://history.churchofjesuschrist.org/article/historic-sites-palmyra-whitmer-farm-fayette.

11. James E. Faust, "The Light in Their Eyes," *Ensign*, November 2005, 22.

12. Jena E. Pincott, "What Your Face Really Reveals about You," *Psychology Today*, November 2012, https://psychologytoday.com/us/articles/201211/what-your-face-really-reveals-about-you.

13. D. Todd Christofferson, "Sustainable Societies," *Ensign*, November 2020, 33.

14. Monson, "Be an Example and a Light," 86–87.

15. Richard L. Evans, *Richard Evans' Quote Book* (Salt Lake City: Publishers Press, 1971), 244.

16. In an article in the *Improvement Era* from August 1942, President Heber J. Grant discusses his correspondence with William George Jordan along with several quotes that he found particularly powerful from Jordan's book *The Power of Truth*. In this article, President Grant also shares the following: "I had one letter from the author [Jordan] expressing the opinion that from his investigation he had become convinced that more than any other religion with which he was familiar, the religion that you and I have espoused and know to be true, yields dividends of better individual lives, and a religion is of value only to the extent to which it improves the individual status of the [one] who holds that religion." See Heber J. Grant, *Improvement Era*, August 1942, 491.

17. William G. Jordan, *Self Control, Its Kingship and Majesty* (New York: Kessinger, 1905), 36–37.

5

Information within Light

Since intelligence . . . corresponds with the main form of energy of the universe, the doctrine of God, and all other beings, and of life, finds expression in terms of energy. That is exactly what science demands. . . . Scientific truth cannot be theological lie. To the sane mind, theology and philosophy must harmonize. They have the common ground of truth on which to meet.[1]

—Elder John A. Widtsoe

I have a love-hate relationship with traveling. In my line of work, I end up making nearly a dozen domestic and a handful of international trips each year, mostly for scientific conferences. I love learning about the cultures, tasting the foods, and taking in the sights of new places. Yet, I hate the absence from my family.

In the early 2000s, I took my first multicountry trip to Asia. For two weeks, communication with my young family amounted to little more than a brief phone call every few days. Granted, we thought it was remarkable to be speaking in real time from across the world, but our brief and often-times poorly connected conversations did little to assuage the pains of being apart.

Fast forward a decade, and I again found myself on a trip to Asia. It had been a long flight—twenty-four hours since I'd left home—and after checking into my hotel room, I longed to see my family. The pain of missing them was compounded by the memory of having left two of my children, who were begging me not to go, in tears as I was leaving for the airport. Unlike the trip from ten years earlier, I didn't need to dig out my international calling card and work through the long process of entering access codes. This time, I could simply grab my smartphone and tap a few icons on the screen. Literally within seconds, my wife and three rambunctious kids were smiling back at me *from 7,000 miles away*. As our boys broke out into a wrestling match over who got to sit closer to the screen, my wife wryly asked whether I was still feeling sad about leaving.

For the remainder of that trip, and all others since then, I have been able to see or speak with my family every single day. What an incredible transformation that I witnessed in just a few years! I have spent a great deal of my scientific career working to improve how this type of communication data is processed once it is received, but the entire progression of how that data had been transmitted through space, under seas, and ultimately into a small handheld unit thousands of miles away became fascinating to me at a whole new level after that conversation between New York and Beijing a few years ago.

In addition to the indispensable gadgets of modern technology, we have light to thank for such communication marvels. Only light could travel fast enough to enable the conversation with my family to take place without long pauses between each statement. And, as it turns out, only light could provide the ability for such large amounts of information to be seamlessly transmitted. How was such information encoded into light, and what are the parallels to spiritual light and the information that is contained within?

How Do We Pack Information into Light?

Imagine the volume of data that was transmitted between my wife's hand-held smartphone in New York and my smartphone in China. There was the audio (our voices) and with it the video (our pictures), each of which consists of thousands of pixels of information for every frame (and there was a dozen or so frames transmitted each second). That is a lot of information! The process for storing this information in light begins with digitization.

To digitize something means to break it down into discrete data points. Computers operate with a binary code (a language) by using the numbers one (1) and zero (0). These binary ones and zeros are the alphabet of the digital world. Basically, everything that is picked up by the phone's microphone is converted into a string of ones and zeros that can be converted back into the original sound by the receiving phone. The same is true for every pixel of every frame that makes up the video—each piece is converted to ones and zeros and then transmitted, received, and converted back to the pixels and frames that make up the video.

Once the audio and video of the conversation is digitized, that string of data must be encoded into light for transmission. This is done by modifying some attribute of the light. For instance, the intensity of the photons that are being transmitted could be modulated (i.e., controllably changed in time), so that a higher number of photons represents a digital one, and a lower number, a digital zero.[2] In this way, pulses of light would carry all the information needed for the video call.[3] This technique is also quite similar to one of the oldest forms of wireless communication: amplitude-modulated (AM) radio waves (which are also light waves). Even without digitizing the information (which is audio in the form of a sound wave), the amplitude of the light is modulated (by changing intensity, as discussed above) to match that of the sound wave. Remember, the *energy/frequency* of the light would not change, just the *amplitude/intensity*.[4]

If this still feels like a lot to process, just remember this: Incredible amounts of data/information can be packed into light. This is done by modifying the photons in a way that represents the correct stream of ones and zeros. The receiver of this information-packed light (in the case of my conversation with my family, this would be our smartphones) must be able to extract the stream of ones and zeros and interpret them. The role of whatever is receiving information-packed light is very important from a privacy and security point of view. For instance, we would prefer our conversations (and all other data for that matter) to be received only by those with whom we are conversing. So, there must be some aspect of the light that ensures that it will be captured only by the intended receiver. In all this, ponder the fact that just because we cannot access certain information in light ourselves does not mean the information is not there (e.g., thousands of cell phone conversations are traveling all around us right now as information-packed light, yet we are completely unaware of them).

What Is Encoded in Spiritual Light?

Since we know a wealth of information can be craftily embedded into light in a way that is only retrievable by the intended receiver, we can now correlate this technological reality with spiritual light. Because each of us has a distinct spirit, we can undoubtedly receive information from spiritual light that is specifically intended for us. If a smartphone, which is human-made technology, is capable of receiving voice, video, and countless other bits of information, imagine what must be possible with God's perfect understanding of light. There is an incredible depth to the information that could be communicated with spiritual light: thoughts, feelings, intentions, directions, scriptures, truths, and so forth. After all, the scriptures teach of the significant connection between light, truth, and knowledge (see Doctrine and Covenants 84:45; 93:28).

All of the above-mentioned information could be encoded in the spiritual light that radiates from us, as well as in the light we may be receiving from others and in the light that is always emanating to us from the presence of God (see Doctrine and Covenants 88:12). One thing I want to be careful of is the insinuation that *all* information transfer between us and God is through light, which may be an oversimplification of how our Father in Heaven communicates with us. For instance, we know that the Holy Ghost most certainly speaks to us in numerous ways; some of these may involve light, but we cannot definitively say they all do. It is certain that light provides a powerful means for communicating so long as we are prepared to extract the information that is sent to us.

Interestingly, the very aspect of spiritual light that makes it distinct from all other forms of light may very well be the information that is encoded within. This distinction makes sense when aligned with the following teaching, repeated in the New Testament and the Doctrine and Covenants: "I am the light which shineth in darkness, and the darkness comprehendeth it not" (Doctrine and Covenants 10:58). Those who are unprepared (not appropriately tuned in) will be unable to extract the information within the spiritual light from the Lord; it will be as if they are in darkness since they are not obtaining any use from the light that is shining. Meanwhile, for those who are prepared and tuned in to the Lord, his spiritual light will enlighten, inspire, teach, and direct them. In short, he will be a light unto their path, as shown in these biblical verses:

> Thy word is a lamp unto my feet, and a light unto my path. (Psalm 119:105)

> Then spake Jesus again unto them, saying, I am the light of the world: he that followeth me shall not walk in darkness, but shall have the light of life. (John 8:12)

On the Same Wavelength

Let's now consider how the information packed into radiated spiritual light may be received and interpreted by others. In a way, this relates to our discussion of sensing spiritual light in chapter 4, but we will now explore how certain connections may be established, and information transferred, between people. For instance, can you recall a time when you thought of someone and then suddenly that person called you on the phone? Or, can you remember when a random memory came to your mind and then seconds later a friend brings up the same memory? Why do these things happen? They could all be written off as coincidences, but to me (as a scientist), an accumulation of coincidences forms the foundation of evidence for some law or process that is at work.

First, let's revisit how a radio works. Music is transmitted from an antenna at a radio station by encoding it into radio waves of light. You then tune the antenna on your radio with a dial or button to receive that specific wavelength of light, and then you listen to the music. If human-kind can make an antenna for resolving audio information from light, just think of the wondrous things the antenna of the soul must be capable of. And this would not be limited to influencing just those within the same room or even the same building as us. Remember, it would take only 0.134 seconds (that's 134 milliseconds) for light to travel all the way around the world![5]

Your mind may be swirling with examples from your own life of when others' thoughts profoundly influenced you from a great distance away. While the science fiction world represents such telepathy as a mystical and oversimplified superpower, I imagine we all have had some very real experiences with someone else's thoughts having a clear, direct impact on us—even from far away. Allow me to share one such experience from my life.

When I was a teenager, the youth in my stake performed a musical fireside of songs primarily from Kenneth Cope's album, *Greater Than Us All*. Under the direction of the wonderful Dudley Barnum (you could not have found a more fun-loving and emotionally invested conductor for the task of rallying a large group of teenagers), we met weekly for a couple months to learn and rehearse the songs. My best friend and I attended every single practice. Neither of us was much of a singer, nor as teenage boys were we the type to express how deeply touching participating in the choir was to us (our consistent attendance was the only evidence of this). My friend and I took different paths not too long after our experience of singing in that youth choir. As a matter of fact, more than twenty years went by, and neither of us had ever mentioned the choir to each other. While we had been at each other's weddings and kept in touch as best we could, it simply never came up.

One day I was sitting at an airport waiting to board a plane when the memory of that choir from twenty years earlier came profoundly to my mind. With the wondrous power of technology at my fingertips, I downloaded the album and started listening to the songs. I couldn't help but think of my friend and that choir and how much those experiences meant to me. Phone in hand and music playing in my ear, I began scrolling through my social media account. Suddenly, I saw a post pop up from this very friend who was serving in the Army and was stationed in Saudi

Arabia, halfway around the world from where I was at that moment. He wasn't particularly active on social media, so imagine my surprise in seeing that not only had he posted something, but more importantly, his post had included a link to one of the songs that we sang in that youth choir. Under the link he wrote this caption: "I remember singing this in our youth group choir about 20 years ago. What a great song and a great feeling." I continue to marvel at the incredible power of our thoughts and how they are able to connect us across thousands of miles, over mountains and across oceans.

There is scriptural context for this radiation of our thoughts, though it often focuses more on the condemning nature of unrighteous thoughts, as in the following verses from the Book of Mormon:

> But this much I can tell you, that if ye do not watch yourselves, and your thoughts, and your words, and your deeds, and observe the commandments of God, and continue in the faith of what ye have heard concerning the coming of our Lord, even unto the end of your lives, ye must perish. And now, O man, remember, and perish not. (Mosiah 4:30)

> Now Zeezrom, seeing that thou hast been taken in thy lying and craftiness, for thou hast not lied unto men only but thou hast lied unto God; for behold, he knows all thy thoughts, and thou seest that thy thoughts are made known unto us by his Spirit; . . .
> . . . For our words will condemn us, yea, all our works will condemn us; we shall not be found spotless; and our thoughts will also condemn us; and in this awful state we shall not dare to look up to our God; and we would fain be glad if we could command the rocks and the mountains to fall upon us to hide us from his presence. (Alma 12:3, 14)

I think most people actually know the power of thoughts even if they haven't considered it in the precise manner I have presented here. After all, how often do we tell others that they will be in our thoughts and, conversely, how often do we feel especially cared for when we learn that others have been thinking of us? Reflect on how common it is to express one's sincere motivations by offering thoughts and prayers in others' behalf. It is interesting that half of this expression is giving something we can offer of ourselves and the other half calls upon God to give what he will.

There is so much more that can be learned from the light we sense than what has been reviewed in the few examples I shared. Thinking on the same wavelength as others, I believe, is only a glimpse of the depth of information available to us as we gain a deeper familiarity with spiritual light. The Holy Ghost amplifies our ability to detect and decipher the light from others (see how Zeezrom's thoughts are made known to Alma and Amulek in Alma 12, cited above) so that the information may be used for our growth and protection.

Discerning Truth from Light

There is one other aspect to the information within spiritual light that is opportune to examine at this point. As previously noted, truth and light are inextricably connected (see Doctrine and Covenants 84:45; 88:6–7; 93:29, 36), so when we say that a person comes to *know* the truth we are effectually saying they have come to *discern* spiritual light associated with that truth. Beyond the thoughts or feelings that may be encoded into the light a person radiates, there is this embedded connection between light and truth. Consider the beauty of this connection through the words of the prophet Alma, who taught that exercising faith—"hop[ing] for things which are not seen, which are true" (Alma 32:21)—would lead to a witness and thus to a knowledge of the truth of those things, but not necessarily to a knowledge of *all* truth:

> And now, behold, is your knowledge perfect? Yea, your knowledge is perfect *in that thing*, and your faith is dormant; and this because you know, for ye know that the word hath swelled your souls, and ye also know that it hath sprouted up, that *your understanding doth begin to be enlightened*, and your mind doth begin to expand.
>
> O then, is not this real? I say unto you, Yea, *because it is light*; and *whatsoever is light, is good, because it is discernible*, therefore ye must know that it is good; and now behold, after ye have tasted this light is your knowledge perfect? (Alma 32:34–35; emphasis added)

From Alma's model, one must first be taught certain truth, choose to believe the truth, exercise faith in that truth, and then receive a witness of the truth (through the Holy Ghost) that yields a perfect knowledge *in that thing* (see Alma 32:34) or in that specific truth—thus discerning the spiritual light associated with that truth. Unlike a human-made radio that is only able to discern information from a specific tuned frequency of radio wave, our souls are clearly able to discern truth from an endless array of light that is growing "brighter and brighter until the perfect day" (Doctrine and Covenants 50:24). A fundamental principle of the spiritual physics of light is that light and truth are inextricably linked; my postulation from this principle is that this link goes deeper than analogy and is related to the encoding of information within spiritual light that can be deciphered by the soul that is in tune, thus bringing about greater knowledge or discernment.

Regarding the importance of choosing to believe in a truth, notice how Alma hinges everything on this principle (see Alma 32:27). How could he not have been thinking about his own agonizing yet marvelous conversion and realizing that so very much pain could have been averted had he been willing to simply believe. For him, there was no question that even a particle of faith could bring the most "marvelous light" (Alma 36:20). This light expands the mind and allows for more truth to be received, believed, and finally discerned. The light of that truth then radiates from the soul and links to the mind in ways that bring understanding and even perfect knowledge *in that thing* (see Alma 32:34).

Considering this in the context of the first hypothesis presented in chapter 3 (that the Holy Ghost is the power source for spiritual light radiation), receiving a witness of a particular truth from the Spirit will power the corresponding spiritual light from the Light of Christ within us. After having that light powered, or after having "tasted this light" (Alma 32:35), is your knowledge perfect or your faith exhausted? Do you now understand all things and have *all* light? No. And why not? Because there is specific light associated with *each* truth. This same pattern must be followed for all truth: we are taught, *then* we choose to believe, *then* we exercise faith in the teaching, *then* we receive a witness from the Holy Ghost (who testifies of all truth/light; see Moroni 10:5), and *then* we are able to discern (and, I would add, radiate) the spiritual light of that truth. Repeating this pattern throughout our lives is to continue in God, always learning and embracing more truth, until the "perfect day": "That which is of God is light; and he that receiveth light, and continueth in God, receiveth more light; and that light groweth brighter and brighter until the perfect day" (Doctrine and Covenants 50:24).

More Depth Than We Know

Scientists continue to study light for its ability to transmit information. This means that our physical understanding of light and how to cram increasingly more data into it, also grows. For example, researchers have recently discovered that photons actually have an additional attribute that had not been detected in all the years we've spent studying light. This attribute, which scientists call "orbital angular momentum," has the potential to dramatically enhance information transmission using light. Theoretically, this newly discovered property of light enables an endless amount of data to be transmitted all at once.[6]

Just think, this incredible property of light has been there all along, and yet we are only recently discovering its existence and implications. What more is there to light that we have yet to decipher with scientific apparatuses? How many further characteristics are present and filled with information that we cannot measure empirically but may detect spiritually?

I close this chapter with some reflection on what we have determined thus far: We all radiate light. An unimaginable depth of information is capable of being encoded into that light. There is no escaping its radiation or its effects—light will influence us and all those around us regardless of whether or not we acknowledge that reality. Distance is no bound for the influence of light; it takes a mere 134 milliseconds for it to travel the distance all the way around the world. Our thoughts, our prayers—even our very beings—are constantly detectable, including a tremendous depth of information and insight accessible to those who are in tune.

As we draw closer to the Lord, we refine our ability to extract valuable, eternal truths from the light we detect. As we strive to be more sensitive to the light that is constantly influencing us, and as we look for and acknowledge the light we detect from others, the Holy Ghost will magnify our abilities to learn from the light: these abilities will ultimately lead us to discern more and more light. For some, it is a gift of the Spirit to be able to decipher insightful information from the light that others radiate. For all, it is something we should strive and pray for so that we can be more useful instruments in the hands of the Lord.

Notes

1. John A. Widtsoe, *Joseph Smith as Scientist* (1908; repr., Grantsville: Archive Publishers, 2000), 155–56.

2. The four most common attributes of light that may be modulated to encode information are amplitude (intensity), frequency, phase, and polarization. We have discussed amplitude and frequency in previous chapters, but phase and polarization are new aspects of light for this book. Phase refers to how one photon lines up with another; basically, if the electromagnetic field that makes up one photon is exactly in sync with that of another photon, they are in phase. If the fields are not in sync, then the photons are out of phase with each other. Transmitting photons that are out of phase in a controlled fashion can be a way for encoding information into light. Finally, polarization refers to the directionality of a photon (e.g., they can be vertically or horizontally polarized); this is often used in sunglass lenses to filter out certain polarizations of light (especially reflected light that can create glare).

3. This is not entirely unlike the transmission of telegrams using Morse code in the original telegraph system (though the telegraph used pulses of electricity rather than light).

4. Note that when a tremendous amount of information needs to be encoded into light (this is what fiber optic cables are used for), more than one attribute of the light may be modulated at once. For instance, the amplitude may be modulated to carry some of the data while differences in phase are also used to send additional information.

5. There would be other important aspects to consider when thinking about whether light would actually circle the earth. While gravity does influence

photons, gravity's effect is too small to actually keep the light in earth's orbit. Hence, for light to be radiated from one side of the world to the other, there would need to be some form of reflection, such as with particles in the atmosphere, that keeps the light moving around the earth.

6. Such infinite cramming of photons to increase the density of data being transmitted by light is based on the fact that photons with different orbital angular momentum (OAM) do not interfere with each other. So, just think of being able to send billions of internet connections all through the same fiber optic cable at the same time. If that doesn't impress you, consider the fact that this application of the OAM of photons to encode data would enable orders of magnitude greater bandwidth for transmitting data than our current technology allows. More information about the orbital angular momentum of light and how it boosts data transmitted with light can be found in the following articles: Alan E. Willner, "Twisted Light Could Dramatically Boost Data Rates," *IEEE Spectrum*, http://spectrum.ieee.org/telecom/wireless/twisted-light-could-dramatically -boost-data-rates; and "'Vortex Microlaser' Encodes Information in Twisting Beams of Light," *Duke Electrical & Computer Engineering*, https://ece.duke.edu /about/news/vortex-microlaser-encodes-information-twisting-beams-light.

6

Light Moving and Burning

God's light includes the physical light we see, which makes us feel so warm and comfortable. . . . In other words, all kinds of light are related to intelligence and truth. [1]

—Elder Theodore M. Burton

When fired from a gun, the average bullet travels at 2,500 feet per second (1,700 miles per hour). This is, for most intents and purposes, ample speed and corresponding momentum for the desired result. However, in some instances, such as military defense applications, a few thousand feet per second is insufficient and leads to unacceptable levels of inaccuracy when it comes to hitting a high-speed target from a long distance. A prominent example is that of missile defense, where it is a complex challenge to shoot down an incoming missile that can be moving at over 11,000 miles per hour at a distance of hundreds of miles away.

Light moves at 980,000,000 feet per second (670,000,000 miles per hour), making it nearly 400,000 times faster than the average bullet. To put this into perspective, consider the fact that in the time it takes a bullet to travel the length of a football field, light could circumnavigate the earth.[2] This staggering advantage of speed, and corresponding accuracy, has motivated the use of light as a sort of weapon. Of course, simply shining a spotlight on an incoming missile would do little to deter the missile from accomplishing its objective; there would need to be some corresponding physical impact—an energy transfer—between the photons of light and the target object. Is light capable of providing such an immense transfer of energy? Could light physically move something or even destroy it?

Light's Momentum

First, consider the ability for light to cause something to burn. This concept is not difficult to accept because most of us have been sunburned at some point in our lives. You can imagine what would happen if you were to increase the energy of light from the sun by 1,000 times and focus it onto a small area—it would burn most anything in its path. This is akin to the classic use of a magnifying glass to concentrate sunlight in order to ignite a piece of paper or dry leaves (hopefully for no more nefarious uses).

What about light physically moving an object? There is a connection between the ability of light to burn something and the possibility that it can cause something to move. Light has momentum that is directly proportional to its energy. Momentum is the ability for something to transfer energy to something else, and it is typically related to the mass and velocity (or speed) of an object. A small car and a large semitruck moving at the same speed would both have momentum; yet, if they were to run into something, the truck would do far greater damage (transfer more energy) than the car because of the truck's larger mass (weight) and thus greater momentum.

For light, a single photon (the smallest particle or component of light) will have very, very little momentum—this doesn't mean that photons have mass (they do not and are referred to as "massless particles"); this is just a fallout of the quantum physics and wave-particle duality of light.[3] Yet, a large number of photons all together (high intensity) could have a reasonable amount of momentum, especially if they are high-energy photons. When a photon of light impacts an object, it has the potential to transfer its momentum to the object (essentially by knocking into the object's atoms). Consequently, if a high-intensity beam of light (lots of photons all packed together) with enough momentum impacts an object, the object *could* be moved.

To get a better idea of how light could move objects, reflect on what it feels like to have a drop of rain fall on your head; it generally doesn't hurt, even though the raindrop has a certain momentum and is thus transferring energy to you. Now think of a fire hose, which shoots enough water with such high speed that it can readily knock a person over. That stream of water from the fire hose is simply a concentration of tiny droplets (like the raindrop) moving at a very high speed; in other words, water from the fire hose has a lot of momentum. The same is true when there is a very high concentration of photons with sufficiently high energy.

The first full articulation of how light, as electromagnetic radiation, may transfer momentum to something was provided by the revolutionary scientist James Clerk Maxwell in 1862.[4] Another term used to describe this momentum transfer from light is *radiation pressure*, which focuses more on the overall effect (pressure) that occurs because of the light (radiation). In astrophysics, the physical principle of light's radiation pressure is pivotal; for instance, without accounting for the radiation pressure from the sun on the Viking space probes that were sent to Mars in the 1970s, the spacecraft would have missed Mars's orbit by over 9,000 miles![5] So, something with a relatively small immediate effect has the potential to make a very sizable long-term or cumulative effect.

There is also a very real, recent example of how concentrated high-energy light is able to heat, move, or just generally damage an object. The United States Navy, working with defense contractor Lockheed Martin, has developed a prototype Laser Weapon System (LaWS) that uses a concentrated beam of high-energy light (a laser) to destroy incoming missiles or other threats.[6] While not completely ready for deployment as of early 2019, video demonstrations of LaWS in action can be viewed online. (If you view it, please notice that you cannot see the beam of laser light because its energy is much higher than the visible region of the electromagnetic spectrum.) An even more recent demonstration of such a laser-based weapon system demonstrates its ability to destroy a flying drone.[7]

While a concentrated high-energy beam of light is only recently becoming accessible to the scientific world, what about the spiritual world? Is there evidence of such a phenomenon being harnessed by the Lord or his servants in scriptural accounts? At the very least, there are compelling examples of this possibility that we will explore throughout the remainder of this chapter.

Samuel the Lamanite—Light Moving Objects

One compelling possibility of light's momentum being used to move objects occurs in the story of Samuel the Lamanite from the Book of Mormon. In a hallmark act of courage and faith, Samuel went among the Nephite people in the city of Zarahemla to preach repentance. In addition to the unpopularity of his message on the ears of a people who were in a state of "great wickedness" (Helaman 13:1), Samuel may have also been dealing with some degree of racial prejudice because of his Lamanite lineage. After spending many unfruitful days preaching around the city, the people unceremoniously cast him out.

Not surprisingly, Samuel set his face toward home—most likely a journey of several days (see Mosiah 22:11, 13). We would hardly think less of Samuel if his story ended there. But the fact is, if his story ended there, we would likely never have heard of him. Who knows how many similarly righteous people of that time accepted calls to preach and were met with little to no success? I'm not suggesting that Samuel was not incredible in his prophetic instruction to the Nephites, but we have nothing to suggest that he was an anomaly up to this point. Even the Nephites who ended up believing his words went and found the prophet Nephi (son of Helaman) to confess their sins and be baptized (see Helaman 16:1). It is what happened when Samuel returned to Zarahemla that made his story a standout.

Just as he was "about to return to his own land," the voice of the Lord came to Samuel and told him to return and prophesy "whatsoever things should come into his heart" (Helaman 13:2–3). Obediently, he tried to go back into the city, but the Nephites would not allow him to enter. With limited options, Samuel decided to climb onto the wall of the city. There is no indication that the voice of the Lord came to him again to instruct him to climb onto the wall; by all counts, this was entirely Samuel's idea. The Lord's instructions had been given: go back and speak what comes to your heart. Knowing he could not do that if they didn't let him in, he decided to find another way. This is reminiscent of Nephi's going back to Jerusalem for the plates of brass, when the instruction from the Lord to get the plates of brass from Laban was also clearly received (and faithfully, not to mention legendarily, accepted in 1 Nephi 3:7). It took two miserable failures to finally have Nephi return to Jerusalem "not knowing before-hand the things which [he] should do" (1 Nephi 4:6); indeed, he did do things he never would have imagined, including slaying Laban by direct command of the Spirit.

I like to think the same is true for Samuel. He never envisioned preaching from the top of a city wall. The walls were possibly those con-structed under the direction of Captain Moroni, who ensured they were "strong and high" (Alma 50:3), even to an "exceeding height" (53:4; see 62:21–22). Samuel had instructions from the Lord, and he was going to follow them at all costs. Perched atop the city wall, he prophesied marvel-ous things, including the signs that would accompany the birth and death of the Savior (see Helaman 13–15). At the conclusion of his message, many believed—but not all. Of the remaining naysayers from the crowd, we learn that those "who did not believe in the words of Samuel were angry with him; and they cast stones at him upon the wall, and also many shot arrows at him as he stood upon the wall" (Helaman 16:2). What happens next can only be described as an absolute miracle: "But the Spirit of the Lord was with [Samuel], insomuch that they could not hit him with their stones neither with their arrows. Now when they saw that they could not hit him, there were many more who did believe on his words, insomuch that they went away unto Nephi to be baptized" (16:2–3).

How do you picture this transpiring? If you're like me, one of the first images that comes to mind is the depiction offered by the artist Arnold Friberg showing Samuel on top of a very high wall, hands outstretched, with a visible aura of light shining around him. Evident in the scene is the deflection of all skillfully aimed stones and arrows, which causes them to miss their target. The mechanism of this divine protection is without explanation and thus is a *miracle*.

At this point, it's worth remembering that God works by laws that govern the universe. While scientific discoveries in mortality may be admittedly limited compared to God's omniscience, they do, nevertheless, contribute to one's increase in knowledge and intelligence. The Lord has made clear that a person's increase in such knowledge will "rise with [them] in the resurrection" and that they "will have so much the advantage in the world to come" (Doctrine and Covenants 130:18–19). This suggests that our scientific knowledge must also have useful eternal significance. As for miracles, great insight is provided by the following statements from Parley P. Pratt and James E. Talmage, respectively:

> Among the popular errors of modern times, an opinion prevails that miracles are events which transpire contrary to the laws of nature, that they are effects without a cause. If such is the fact, there never has been a miracle, and there never will be one. The laws of nature are the laws of truth. Truth is unchangeable, and independent in its own sphere. A law of nature never has been broken. And it is an absolute impossibility that such law ever should be broken.[8]

> Miracles are commonly regarded as occurrences in opposition to the laws of nature. Such a conception is plainly erroneous, for the laws of nature are inviolable. However, as human understanding of these laws is at best but imperfect, events strictly in accordance with natural law may appear contrary thereto. The entire constitution of nature is founded on system and order.[9]

Could Samuel's protection have come from a very localized, heavy gust of wind? Perhaps, though Samuel's balance must have been impeccable to withstand it, and it seems that such a rushing wind would have been more obvious to the stone-slinging multitude. The fact is that the naysayers in the crowd were so baffled by Samuel's miraculous protection that they declared, "he hath a devil; and because of the power of the devil which is in him we cannot hit him with our stones and our arrows" (Helaman 16:6). This is an iniquitous way of saying that they had no idea how he was being protected. Certainly there could have been some other not yet understood physical force invoked by the Lord to aid Samuel.

Notice that the scripture cites the "Spirit of the Lord" being with Samuel as the reason for his protection (Helaman 16:2). Another name for the Spirit of the Lord can be the Spirit of truth (see John 14:17; 15:26; 16:13; Doctrine and Covenants 6:15; 50:17–22).[10] After all, it is by the Spirit that one comes to *know* the truth. The Lord also declared that his "Spirit *is* truth; . . . and if it be in you it shall abound" (Doctrine and Covenants 88:66; emphasis added). Now, to bring this all together, consider these verses from the Doctrine and Covenants: "And whatsoever is truth is light, and whatsoever is light is Spirit, even the Spirit of Jesus Christ. And the Spirit giveth light to every man that cometh into the world; and the Spirit enlighteneth every man through the world, that hearkeneth to the voice of the Spirit" (84:45–46).

As Samuel stood unflinchingly on that high city wall, having hearkened to the voice of the Spirit that instructed him to return to Zarahemla and speak the words that would be put into his heart, the light of the Lord was most certainly upon him. As the stones and arrows began to fly, protection was provided for the Lord's servant. In modern times, human-made technology uses beams of light to destroy missiles and flying drones moving at hundreds of miles per hour; could not the spiritual light of the omniscient and omnipotent Lord have been used to deflect some stones and arrows from hitting Samuel the Lamanite?

One other point that is reinforced by Samuel's story is the power of each individual in the service of the Lord. It's not as if the Nephites of Zarahemla were devoid of an inspired preacher prior to Samuel's arrival. Living among them was the prophet Nephi (son of Helaman), who was "baptizing, and prophesying, and preaching, crying repentance unto the people, showing signs and wonders, working miracles among the people" (Helaman 16:4). Samuel's was not necessarily a message that only he could bring to the people. What Samuel uniquely brought was *Samuel*! By doing all to fulfill his assignment from the Lord, Samuel became an instrument for the Lord and brought about the conversion of many people.

So it is with all of us. As we are given opportunities to serve in the Church or in other aspects of our lives, it may not seem clear what it is that we will be able to do to make a difference. What is asked of us is that we do all we can to follow our call to serve (see 2 Nephi 25:23). Oftentimes, this can require perseverance through seemingly insurmountable obstacles related to our perceived inadequacies, challenging circumstances, or lack of ideas. If you learn just one thing from Samuel's story, it should be that God is capable of amplifying your efforts in ways that you can't possibly imagine. When the arrows and stones started flying from the streets of Zarahemla two thousand years ago, Samuel may have been just as surprised as those who threw them when they didn't find their mark. He was prepared to do anything and everything it took to fulfill the Lord's command. It is certain that as we do so, God's light will also shine through us to bring about his purposes.

Abinadi—Light Moving People

It seems that some of the most miraculous events transpire after prophets are commanded to return to the cities that had previously rejected them. In similar fashion to Samuel the Lamanite, the prophet Abinadi had been cast out of the city in which the wicked king Noah ruled. The passage of two years and the addition of a disguise did not keep Abinadi safe for long when he returned to preach the remainder of the Lord's message to the people. It's interesting that Abinadi returned to the city in disguise since it suggests that he also did not know "beforehand the things which [he] should do" (1 Nephi 4:6), just like Nephi and Samuel. It is in such a state that the Lord is most able to use us as an instrument in his hands.

After angering the city's crowd, whose spiritual eyes were still as "blinded" (Mosiah 11:29) as they were on his last visit, Abinadi was taken before King Noah. Following a brief interchange with King Noah's priests, the king pronounced that Abinadi was "mad" and should be slain (13:1):

> And they stood forth and attempted to lay their hands on [Abinadi]; but he withstood them, and said unto them:
>
> Touch me not, for God shall smite you if ye lay your hands upon me, for I have not delivered the message which the Lord sent me to deliver; . . .

Now it came to pass after Abinadi had spoken these words that the people of king Noah durst not lay their hands on him, for *the Spirit of the Lord was upon him*; and *his face shone with exceeding luster*, even as Moses' did while in the mount of Sinai, while speaking with the Lord.

And he spake with power and authority from God; and he continued his words, saying:

Ye *see* that ye have not power to slay me, therefore I finish my message. (Mosiah 13:2–3, 5–7; emphasis added)

Abinadi's visibly shining face is an obvious involvement of light in this scene. The precise cause is not entirely known, though other situations where faces have shone involved Moses communing with the Lord (see Exodus 34:30, 34–35) or the Savior being transfigured—"his face did shine as the sun, and his raiment was white as the light" (Matthew 17:2). Many have noted that when the Prophet Joseph Smith was receiving revelation, he took on a whiteness and brightness in appearance. For instance, Brigham Young recorded, "[Joseph] preached by the Spirit of revelation, and taught in his council by it, and those who were acquainted with him could discover it at once, for at such times there was a peculiar clearness and transparency in his face."[11]

Without question, the spirit of revelation was upon Abinadi as he stood before King Noah and his apostate court. Abinadi would go on to prophesy many future events that came to pass as dictated. Aside from the unmistakable shining of Abinadi's face, what else happened in this scene? The record says that the members of the court "attempted to lay their hands on him" (Mosiah 13:2), but the next thing we know is that Abinadi commands them not to touch him. Did they touch him before that command was given? It is uncertain, but it is clear that they were attempting to do so prior to Abinadi's reproach and that after he spoke, "the people of king Noah durst not lay their hands on him" (13:5). Wouldn't you think it had to be more than the luster of Abinadi's face and his rebuking words that stopped the adrenaline-charged group from obeying the king's command?

In fact, when Abinadi begins speaking again he acknowledges, "Ye see that ye have not power to slay me" (Mosiah 13:7). This confirms that indeed the people of King Noah were set to carry out the king's order to slay Abinadi, perhaps right then and there. We are left to decipher how the events transpired between King Noah's command to "slay [Abinadi]" (13:1) and Abinadi's indication that they had no power to slay him (see 13:7). The readiest conclusion is that the people who attempted to grab or perhaps even slay Abinadi experienced some adverse physical reaction that led them to realize they could not slay him even if they tried (see 1 Nephi 17:52–55 for a similar example of divine protection).

This possible explanation of the scene with Abinadi before King Noah is certainly the one that all of the artists, to my knowledge, have envisioned. As with Samuel the Lamanite, the most famous depiction of Abinadi comes from Arnold Friberg, whose portrayal of these few verses shows King Noah's guards rather violently tossed about the room with details such as a broken sword, helmet on the ground, spilled goblet, and quivering soldier. Another prolific artist, Jeremy Winborg, likewise shows a room with soldiers splayed onto the ground with hands raised defensively. Considering the logical, as well as the artistically depicted, support, we now must ask whether there is any scriptural evidence that some force knocked the advancing soldiers back.[12]

As was the case with Samuel the Lamanite, the only inference to the source of Abinadi's protection is that "the Spirit of the Lord was upon him" (Mosiah 13:5; see Helaman 16:2). Following the above discussion that established that the Spirit equals truth and truth equals light, as indicated in Doctrine and Covenants 84:45–46, we are left to ponder on possible causes of Abinadi's divine protection. As indicated in the quote from Elder Theodore M. Burton at the heading of this chapter:

> God's light includes the physical light we see, which makes us feel so warm and comfortable. God's light is also the power to understand and comprehend all things. In other words, all kinds of light are related to intelligence and truth. . . .
>
> The light of Christ therefore includes not only spiritual light but also physical light, and is a key to understanding that form of energy which is represented by the light we see all around us.[13]

It is compelling how Elder Burton teaches that the light we see all around us is only a representation of the "form of energy" that light is, both spiritually and physically. He makes a direct connection to the Light of Christ, which was also referred to in Doctrine and Covenants 84:45–46 (quoted previously).

We know that the Spirit of the Lord was upon Abinadi, but does this refer to the Light of Christ? Typically, the context of a verse makes the intended usage evident. For instance, in 2 Nephi 26:11, it is mentioned that the "Spirit of the Lord will not always strive with man;" this refers to the Holy Ghost, whose influence diminishes when wickedness abounds. But what of this experience that Abinadi is having? Or, how about that of Samuel the Lamanite? In both cases, it is the Spirit of the Lord being upon or with them that is cited as the reason for their protection.

Whether it was the Holy Ghost, the Light of Christ, or some combination of both working within and around Abinadi to protect him may not matter all that much. The fact is that he was divinely protected. I don't think any of us, with our belief that God is omnipotent, would have doubted God's ability to protect Abinadi. Considered alongside the story of Samuel the Lamanite, Abinadi's experience shows that heavenly protection is accessible to those who have the Spirit of the Lord upon them. As we dedicate ourselves to the service of the Lord, doing all in our power to follow or carry out the missions, callings, assignments, and inspirations that he gives to us, then we may also be divinely protected.

While some of the commandments God asks us to follow may be applicable to all, such as the Ten Commandments or the law of chastity, most often commandments are personal, as with Abinadi's call to preach to the people of King Noah. The covenants we renew each week as we partake of the sacrament remind us of this reality. My mother-in-law, a spiritually wise and insightful person, once taught me that in the sacramental prayer over the bread, we promise to "keep his commandments which he hath given [us]" (Moroni 4:3; emphasis added). This renewal of our covenants is a personal one between the Lord and us; hence, the commandments referred to in the prayer must also include those communicated personally to and for us to accomplish. This would mean returning to preach to wicked Nephites if you were Samuel, or standing as a witness of truth in King Noah's court if you were Abinadi. As we keep these commandments, the promise is clear because it is the only specified promise to us in both of the sacramental prayers, "that

[we] may always have his Spirit to be with [us]" (Moroni 4:3; see 5:2). As Samuel's and Abinadi's miraculous experiences attest, having the Spirit of the Lord with us is of the utmost value in ways that we often cannot even imagine.

Second Coming—Light Burning

Thus far, we determined that there is a proven physical ability for a beam of light to move and burn objects if the light is of sufficiently high energy and intensity. We then considered the Lord's protection of his servants by effecting the physical movement of objects or people. Now let's turn our attention toward the "great and dreadful day of the Lord"[14] and consider the role of light in the Master's Second Coming.

Heavenly visitations, whether from angels or from the Savior himself, are frequently accompanied (and typically preceded) by very bright light. Here are a few examples:

Lehi

> And it came to pass that he saw One descending out of the midst of heaven, and he beheld that his luster was above that of the sun at noon-day. (1 Nephi 1:9)

Saul/Paul

> At midday, O king, I saw in the way a light from heaven, above the brightness of the sun, shining round about me and them which jour-neyed with me. (Acts 26:13)

Joseph Smith—First Vision

> I saw a pillar of light exactly over my head, above the brightness of the sun, which descended gradually until it fell upon me. (Joseph Smith—History 1:16)

Joseph Smith—Moroni's visit

> While I was thus in the act of calling upon God, I discovered a light appearing in my room, which continued to increase until the room was lighter than at noonday, when immediately a personage appeared at my bedside, standing in the air, for his feet did not touch the floor. (Joseph Smith—History 1:30)

As with these examples, the Second Coming of the Lord will most definitely be attended by the most glorious light—light even as "lightning cometh out of the east" (Matthew 24:27). I think it's safe to assume most Christians do envision an overwhelming brightness of light as a key aspect of the Lord's glorious return. What may not be considered is the physical impact this light will have.

Let's face it, many of the scriptures on the Second Coming strike mostly dread and fear into our hearts because the verses discuss the burning and destruction that will take place:

> And then shall appear the sign of the Son of man in heaven: and then shall all the tribes of the earth mourn, and they shall see the Son of man coming in the clouds of heaven with power and great glory. (Matthew 24:30)

> And also that which was written by the prophet Malachi: For, behold, the day cometh that shall burn as an oven, and all the proud, yea, and all that do wickedly, shall be stubble; and the day that cometh shall burn them up, saith the Lord of hosts, that it shall leave them neither root nor branch. (Doctrine and Covenants 133:64)

> For the hour is nigh and the day soon at hand when the earth is ripe; and all the proud and they that do wickedly shall be as stubble; and I will burn them up, saith the Lord of Hosts, that wickedness shall not be upon the earth. (Doctrine and Covenants 29:9)

> Behold, vengeance cometh speedily upon the inhabitants of the earth, a day of wrath, a day of burning, a day of desolation, of weeping, of mourning, and of lamentation; and as a whirlwind it shall come upon all the face of the earth, saith the Lord. (Doctrine and Covenants 112:24)

This picture of the Lord returning to the earth with a type of flame-thrower while burning nearly all in his path has never felt right to me. I just don't see the Lord as one to carry out such a heinous act leading to this awful, heart-wrenching scene. We must remember that this is the God of love and life and mercy! The very heart of his Atonement for humankind was that all would be saved and return to live with our Father. Anything short of us all returning to live with Heavenly Father is saddening to him at a depth and degree I do not think we are able to comprehend. No one observed this more profoundly than the prophet Enoch:

> And it came to pass that the God of heaven looked upon the residue of the people, and he wept; and Enoch bore record of it, saying: How is it that the heavens weep, and shed forth their tears as the rain upon the mountains?
>
> And Enoch said unto the Lord: How is it that thou canst weep, seeing thou art holy, and from all eternity to all eternity? . . .
>
> The Lord said unto Enoch: Behold these thy brethren; they are the workmanship of mine own hands, and I gave unto them their knowledge, in the day I created them; and in the Garden of Eden, gave I unto man his agency; . . .
>
> . . . and the whole heavens shall weep over them, even all the workmanship of mine hands; wherefore should not the heavens weep, seeing these shall suffer? (Moses 7:28–29, 32, 37)

Don't get me wrong. I'm not suggesting that the Lord or his servants did not mean what they said when they prophesied of the impending destruction that will occur at the Second Coming. I do most definitely believe those teachings. What I am saying is that *how* the devastating destruction will occur is also important to understand. A proper realization of what will cause the burning of the Earth transforms the prophecies from threats to warnings and the Lord from ruthless to heartbroken.

There are two key pieces to this: an overwhelming brightness of light will be present at the Second Coming *and* the earth will burn with fire and destruction. All that is missing is the realization that these two aspects of the Lord's return *are connected*. This has actually been taught with great clarity in the scriptures (though much less frequently than the doctrine that focuses strictly on burning and destruction):

> Then will ye longer deny the Christ, or *can ye behold the Lamb of God?* . . . For behold, *when ye shall be brought to see* your nakedness before God, and also the glory of God, and the holiness of Jesus Christ, *it will kindle a flame of unquenchable fire upon you.* (Mormon 9:3, 5; emphasis added)

> For a desolating scourge shall go forth among the inhabitants of the earth, and shall continue to be poured out from time to time, if they repent not, until the earth is empty, and the inhabitants thereof are consumed away and utterly destroyed *by the brightness of my coming.* (Doctrine and Covenants 5:19; emphasis added)

We are striving to be ready to live with God again. As we come to discern more and more light, we prepare ourselves for the intensity of light that will accompany the Lord's Second Coming. That way, when he appears, we will be able to be in his presence without it kindling a burning flame within us. Those who are not prepared, who have not accustomed themselves to the light of the Lord, will be burned by that light. In a way, this is similar to what happens after you have been sitting in a dark room and then suddenly a bright spotlight is shined in your face; however, the brightness at the Second Coming will be orders of magnitude more powerful to those who have chosen to remain in the darkness of unbelief.

To me, it is helpful to think that the destruction at the Second Coming is not the Lord carrying out revenge for rebellion or disobedience but is rather a natural consequence based on the laws of light. I feel like the Savior knew this, and his prophets knew and know this as well. Hence, they have extensively pleaded and prophesied regarding the need for us to prepare and be faithful and obedient so that we may grow in our spiritual light and know that "when [the Lord] shall appear, we shall be like him; for we shall see him as he is" (1 John 3:2). Indeed, the "veil of darkness shall soon be rent" (Doctrine and Covenants 38:8), and we must be purified by, and thus prepared to endure, his light in order to "abide the day" (Malachi 3:2).

Light, for all its intangibility, has considerable potential to burn or move objects. With sufficient energy and intensity, light can be a versatile and powerful tool. Whether or not God used light in the protection of his servants Samuel and Abinadi, or any others, is less consequential than the realization that *he could have*. Noting this allows us to reimagine the Second Coming of our Lord. Concerning the horrific destruction that has been so clearly prophesied, we can ascribe greater emphasis to the workings of natural law rather than to wrathful vengeance for causing the fear of that day for those who are unprepared to be in the presence of God.

Notes

1. Theodore M. Burton, "Light and Truth," *Ensign*, May 1981, 29.

2. As mentioned in previous chapters, there would be other important aspects to consider when thinking about whether light would actually circle the earth. While gravity does influence photons, the effect is too small to actually keep the light in earth's orbit. Hence, for light to be radiated from one side of the world to the other, there would need to be some form of reflection, such as reflection from particles in the atmosphere, that keeps the light moving around the earth.

3. This concept of a photon having no mass yet still having momentum is one of the many conundrums of quantum mechanics. In the laws of classical physics, momentum is equal to mass times velocity (as illustrated with the analogy of a semitruck versus a car given in the text); even in this classical case, keep in mind that the law of conservation of energy is obeyed and that, at its heart, momentum is really about energy transfer from one thing to another (e.g., from a moving car to the object it encounters). For photons, energy is also conserved, which means it can be transferred (from/to the photon), and thus there is momentum. Since it has no mass, the momentum of a photon is dependent directly on its energy; this is most commonly expressed as an inverse dependence on the photon's wavelength: momentum (p) equals Planck's constant (h) divided by wavelength (λ), $p = h/\lambda$. So, in summary, photons have energy that must be conserved, meaning it must either be retained or transferred, and a transfer of their energy to something else is a manifestation of their momentum. If all of this about a massless particle somehow having momentum still feels

confusing, don't worry, you are in good company with all who have ventured into the world of quantum physics!

4. James Clerk Maxwell was responsible for a great deal of the early development of electromagnetic theory and was credited as the first to bring together the forces of electricity, magnetism, and light into one interrelated formalism. It is Maxwell who first determined that light was a construct of electric and magnetic fields and that such electromagnetic radiation moved at a constant speed: the speed of light. His work is often regarded as being the foundation of modern physics, from which the works of special relativity and quantum mechanics were developed. Maxwell was a brilliant and intriguing person who contributed to a vast range of scientific fields—including color theory and bridge trusses—despite his untimely death at the age of forty-eight. See Basil Mahon, *The Man Who Changed Everything: The Life of James Clerk Maxwell* (Hoboken, NJ: Wiley, 2004).

5. Eugene Hecht, *Optics* (Reading, MA: Addison-Wesley, 2001), 57.

6. Tom Risen, "Weapons of the Future, Available Soon," *U.S. News & World Report*, http://usnews.com/news/articles/2015/04/21/us-navy-tests-laser-weapons.

7. David Choi, "Watch this US Navy ship destroy a flying drone with a laser weapon," *Business Insider*, May 2020, https://businessinsider.com/us-navy-ship-destroys-drone-with-laser-weapon-2020-5.

8. Parley P. Pratt, *Key to the Science of Theology* (London: F. D. Richards, 1855), 100.

9. James E. Talmage, *The Articles of Faith* (Salt Lake City: Deseret Book, 1899), 222.

10. The Spirit of the Lord can also at times refer to the Light of Christ, which adds yet another fascinating connection between Samuel's protection and light. This possible connection could be given an entire discussion of its own (as in chapter 3), but focus is given here to the Spirit of truth.

11. Brigham Young, in *Journal of Discourses* (London: Latter-day Saints' Book Depot, 1881), 9:89.

12. There are other noteworthy instances in the scriptures when people are physically knocked down by an unseen force. One occurs in John's account of when Judas, with a band of men and officers, approached Jesus to betray him. After Jesus asks whom they are seeking, they answered, "Jesus of Nazareth," to which the Lord replied, "I am he" (John 18:5). "As soon then as he had said unto them, I am he, they went backward, and fell to the ground" (18:6).

13. Burton, "Light and Truth," 29.

14. There are several references to the "great and dreadful day of the Lord" through-
    out the scriptures that are primarily associated with the prophecy of the prophet
    Malachi. See Malachi 4:5; 3 Nephi 25:5; Doctrine and Covenants 2:1; 110:14, 16.

7

Purifying Power of Light

During the first nineteen months of my life I had caught glimpses of broad green fields, a luminous sky, trees and flowers which the darkness that followed could not wholly blot out. If we have once seen, "the day is ours, and what the day has shown."[1]

—Helen Keller

I love to go backpacking deep in the woods—the more remote the trail, the better. However, remoteness does have certain challenges, including the need to pack sufficient supplies (particularly water) for long stretches. During a multiday backpacking trip in the Blue Ridge Mountains with the young men in my ward, we experienced an exceptionally long day of hiking with virtually no watering holes. The trail map had shown several tributaries crossing our path that day, but all of them turned out to be completely dry. Finally, by late afternoon, we reached our destination for the night: a river. The heat and exhaustion of a long, hot day caused most of us to collapse at the bank of the river, scrambling to fill our water bottles.

As much as we would have liked to drink deeply from the cool flowing river, we all knew the consequences of drinking unpurified water. Most of us fumbled with small pouches that, when filled, allowed you to push the water through a straw-like filter that removed nearly all microbial contaminants. The pouches were cumbersome to fill and the water passed through the filter slowly, making the entire process rather painful. As I impatiently worked with my pouch and water filter, I watched longingly as one of my fellow leaders swiftly scooped a liter of water into an open bottle and inserted a small pen-like device with a glowing light at the end: an ultraviolet (UV) water purifier. About one minute later, he was chugging his newly purified liter of water and crouching down for a refill before I had tasted more than one or two mouthfuls of my own filtered water.

The concept of a filter with microscopic openings that catches potentially harmful contaminants in water is something fairly straightforward to understand. But what about purification of water with UV light? The ability of UV light to purify water is something made possible by a property of light we discussed in the previous chapter: momentum. Each photon of light has a certain energy and some amount of momentum (recall how light is both like a wave [intangible] and a particle [tangible]). With sufficient energy and intensity, light can be used to destroy microorganisms.

Purification with UV Light

Let's break down this process of purification with UV light. First of all, ultraviolet refers to the wavelength of the light. It is called ultra*violet* because its wavelength falls just below that of the visible violet (or purple) light range. Because the energy of light is inversely related to its wavelength, UV light has higher energy than visible light. Light with higher energy means light with more potential to do damage (transfer more energy) when it hits something. In this case, when the UV light hits microorganisms, it causes damage; specifically, the UV light destroys nucleic acids, disrupting the microorganisms' DNA and thus eliminating the ability for them to reproduce. Basically, the UV light is genetically mutating microorganisms, making UV light a mutagen or a germicide. Hence, this process of UV light purification is often referred to as "ultraviolet germicidal irradiation" (UVGI).

If you're wondering whether this type of UV light exposure would be harmful to humans, the answer is certainly yes. This is the exact way a sunburn occurs, although the energy range of UV light used in UVGI is not the same as that of the UV light that causes sunburns. Virtually all of the germicidal UV light from the sun is filtered out by our atmosphere (otherwise, there would be no living microorganisms on earth, and some of them are actually very good!).

Today, UVGI is used as one of the foremost water purification processes. A recent example of this use is the Catskill-Delaware Water Ultraviolet Disinfection Facility that opened in 2013. This facility uses 56 energy-efficient UV reactors to treat 2.2 billion gallons of water per day, water that will subsequently supply the millions of people living in New York City. Even better, the uses of UVGI extend beyond water purification; indeed, there is application for UVGI for food and air purification as well. The concept is similar: UV light is used to destroy potentially harmful microorganisms in a substance or environment.

Purification with Spiritual Light

The fact that light can be used to purify physical substances or environments by destroying impurities is a very compelling attribute. I propose that a similar purifying power is possible with spiritual light. It may not destroy microorganisms in the way UV light does, but there are analogous impurities of the soul, ingested through sin or doubt, and the purifying power of light can cleanse us from these harmful contaminants.

Scriptures teach that we are purified by applying the atoning blood of Christ (see Mosiah 4:2) and that purification is connected to being clean (see Alma 5:21; Doctrine and Covenants 50:28–29). Many scriptural teachings about purification focus on purifying the heart:

> But purify your hearts before me. (Doctrine and Covenants 112:28)

> Yea, purify your hearts, and cleanse your hands and feet before me, that I may make you clean. (Doctrine and Covenants 88:74)

> Apply the atoning blood of Christ that we may receive forgiveness of
> our sins, and our hearts may be purified. (Mosiah 4:2)

> Nevertheless they did fast and pray oft, and did wax stronger and stron-
> ger in their humility, and firmer and firmer in the faith of Christ, unto
> the filling their souls with joy and consolation, yea, even to the purify-
> ing and the sanctification of their hearts, which sanctification cometh
> because of their yielding their hearts unto God. (Helaman 3:35)

As for the role of spiritual light in this purification process, the Lord
teaches that "the glory of God is intelligence, or, in other words, light and
truth. Light and truth forsake that evil one" (Doctrine and Covenants
93:36–37). As we learn and embrace more truth and as we radiate the
associated spiritual light, there is a purifying effect since the evil one is
forsaken by our light. This has interesting ties to one of the hypotheses
from chapter 3 about how spiritual light is generated from within us and
that the Holy Ghost is the source of energy that fuels our radiation of light
based on our righteousness (i.e., our reduced resistance to the Spirit). This
would mean that receiving the Holy Ghost and radiating more and more
light (through our continuing in God—see 50:24) would purify our hearts
by "forsak[ing] that evil one" (93:37). In other words, the Holy Ghost cat-
alyzes our sanctification by fueling our radiation of truth and light, which
purifies us and is made possible by the Atonement of Jesus Christ:

> Now this is the commandment: Repent, all ye ends of the earth, and
> come unto me and be baptized in my name, that ye may be sanctified
> by the reception of the Holy Ghost, that ye may stand spotless before
> me at the last day. (3 Nephi 27:20)

So, what exactly is a person with a purified heart capable of doing?
Foremost, they will "abide the day of [the Lord's] coming" (Doctrine
and Covenants 35:21; see 38:8); they will "stand spotless before [him]"
(3 Nephi 27:20); and they will "be like him, for [they] shall see him as he
is" (Moroni 7:48). (This is a topic for much further discussion in the next
chapter of this book.) There is little doubt that our spiritual purification
has many implications leading up to our preparation for the Lord's Second

Coming. I would like to focus the remainder of this chapter on just one of these implications: increased discernment.

Just as the purification of water using UVGI does not happen instantaneously, our spiritual purification is also not abrupt or immediate. As we draw closer to God, we gain more light, even an increase in the light that we radiate. We previously discussed how this radiated light may affect others and even carry distinct information. But how does this light we radiate influence us? Consider what happens to your physical sight when you are in a dimly lit room and the light is turned up to a higher intensity: greater discernment of your surroundings. Details of which you were previously unaware suddenly become clear. The same outcome must be expected from an increase in our spiritual light: improved discernment of truth and our spiritual surroundings; in short, a more purified perspective.

Discerning Spiritual Light

What does it mean to discern spiritual light? As we ponder this question, recall that those without the gospel frequently *sense* light as they notice something distinct, perhaps even bright, about someone who is setting a righteous example. However, sensing or detecting the spiritual light does not necessarily imply recognition or, more completely, *discernment* of that light. For instance, noticing that the light has become brighter in the room is sensing a change, but looking around to see how the increased light has improved your perspective is discerning that change. Hence, discernment is more than simple detection since it entails an understanding of what is sensed.

Simply sensing spiritual light may help to break down barriers that keep one from believing truths, but full discernment of light requires understanding, and thus learning, of the truths associated with the light. Accountability to God (*discernment* of his light) requires an understanding of his laws. This is a core aspect of the physics of spiritual light: discernment requires understanding of truth. Think about this doctrine, which is found in several places throughout the scriptures, including in John 1:5: "And the light shineth in darkness; and the darkness comprehended it not." The light John is referring to is the Savior. Spiritual light suddenly shining in darkness does not bring comprehension or discernment. I imagine this is like being in a dark room and suddenly having a very bright flashlight turned on and aimed directly at you. Does that bring discernment of your surroundings? No, it mostly just brings frustration and perhaps even pain. However, do you know that the light is there? Most definitely. You have *sensed* the presence of the light, but you have not been able to *discern* anything because of it; what is in the darkness around you remains incomprehensible (i.e., we comprehend it not).

A further point regarding this verse in John 1 is that darkness cannot *do* anything because darkness *is* *nothing* but the absence of light. It is simply a void, or in some cases a veil (see Doctrine and Covenants 38:8; Moses 7:26). The language of the verse in John 1:5 is not suggesting that darkness could ever have actually comprehended the light; rather, if the light were to be *discerned* (through the understanding of associated truth) then it could have "chase[d] darkness" away (Doctrine and Covenants 50:25), thus effecting comprehension. Think of it this way: those who have discerned light will radiate that light—in our analogy of the dark room, they will be holding the flashlight instead of having it aimed directly at their faces. With the flashlight in hand, they can use the light to chase darkness away and comprehend other things; they have come to *know* truth because of their discernment of spiritual light.

Discernment "Set[s] [Our] Spirit[s] Free"

One of the most incredible examples of the transformative effect of discernment is found in the life of Helen Keller. Rather than being a story of how sin or some other impurity was cleansed in order to bring light and discernment, Helen's purification came in the form of receiving and acting on instruction from her devoted teacher, Anne Sullivan. Helen's story illustrates the power of true discernment—particularly how it is so much more than what we take in from our senses.

When she was nineteen months old, Helen Keller's world was plunged into darkness. Blindness and deafness were the results of an illness that had very nearly taken her life. Just imagine, a child still striving to grasp the fundamental processes of life and language, relying mostly on the familiar sight of her parents' faces or well-known sound of their voices, but suddenly being shut out completely from all sight and sound.

If you happen to be unfamiliar with Keller's amazing story, I think it is inspiring to tell the end from the beginning. This remarkable woman went on to become a prolific writer, successful advocate for women's rights, gifted lecturer, and the first deaf and blind person to earn a bachelor's degree. She developed the ability to communicate fluidly by placing her hand over a person's mouth and throat, interpreting the combination of lip movement and throat vibration into words, then applying these techniques in reverse to speak. But how was all of this possible? How could someone who is cut off from two of the most fundamental senses be capable of so much? In part, Keller's exceptional genius undoubtedly played a role. However, genius alone could not have made such a successful life possible in her situation.

In one of the most inspiring stories of loving mentorship of all time (and one that has been depicted in several play and film adaptations), Helen had a teacher who pulled her from the darkness and into the light. Anne Sullivan was brought into Helen's life when she was six years old, and Sullivan began the laborious process of bridging the gap between Helen's lonely, dark world and the people, objects, and feelings that surrounded her. Sullivan began by helping Helen understand that every object she interacted with had a specific name associated with it; a very basic concept that was far outside of Helen's grasp since she had not learned to speak before losing her vision and hearing. Being shut out from the most common social cues, such as pointing to an object and saying its name, made this an incredibly challenging task. The breakthrough came when Sullivan held Helen's hand under cool running water and then slowly and carefully spelled out, letter by letter, the word W-A-T-E-R into the little girl's hand over and over again. Helen recalls her complete euphoria when she realized that the symbols being marked in her hand were a unique representation of the water and, further, that everything had its own such representation (or word). The ensuing months were filled with Helen's insatiable longing to learn the words for anything and everything she could find!

Helen's story of coming to discern the world around her is one of the most powerful examples of someone being brought from darkness (of any type) into the light. Keller reflected, "Gradually I got used to the silence and darkness that surrounded me and forgot that it had ever been different, until she came—my teacher—who was to set my spirit free."[2] It is also a story that palpably captures how the power of light extends beyond physical sight. Through the guidance of her teacher, Helen was gradually able to discern the world around her. Once, Elder D. Todd Christofferson related Helen Keller's story and the influential role of her teacher, Anne Sullivan. Then he added this counsel: "Similarly, as we come to trust rather than resist our divine Teacher, He can work with us to enlighten and lift us to a new reality. . . . Each of us can experience the ecstasy of divine potential unfolding within us, much like the joy Helen Keller felt when words came to life, *giving light to her soul* and setting it free."[3]

When Keller was twenty-three years old, she published her first autobiography, *The Story of My Life*, and in it she frequently mentions how things look or the beauty of the scenery that she has seen in her travels around the country. It struck me at first as odd that someone who has virtually never seen or heard would be able to describe, and with touching detail, the beauties and sounds of her surroundings. At one point, she addresses this oddity—undoubtedly expecting this uncertainty from her readers—as she describes a trip that she took to visit the great Niagara Falls:

> We went to Niagara in March, 1893. It is difficult to describe my emotions when I stood on the point which overhangs the American Falls and felt the air vibrate and the earth tremble.
>
> It seems strange to many people that I should be impressed by the wonders and beauties of Niagara. They are always asking: "What does this beauty or that music mean to you? You cannot see the waves rolling up the beach or hear their roar. What do they mean to you?" In the most evident sense they mean everything. I cannot fathom or define their meaning any more than I can fathom or define love or religion or goodness.[4]

Keller had advanced from being a child whose world was veiled in darkness (with only a handful of invented signs for her basic needs), to being able to sense the beauty, power, and majesty of Niagara Falls and describe it with as much emotion and fervor as the most observant seeing and hearing person. Honestly, Keller seemed to experience the world around her to a fullness that most seeing and hearing people do not even come close to realizing. Why is that? Surely we gain much by our ability to see and hear; yet Keller seemed to reach an unmatched depth of connection to her surroundings.

Keller's experience with discernment truly exemplifies the unseen power of light on our souls. She always had the potential to discern things about the people she met and places she visited, but she needed the power of "light to her soul" to activate such discernment. The same is true for each of us, spiritually. Within us all is the divine potential for discerning or comprehending "all things" (Doctrine and Covenants 88:67). Activating this discernment requires the purifying power of spiritual light, even so much that our "whole bodies [are] filled with light" (88:67). As we follow the pattern for discerning spiritual light, we are given a perspective on the world around us that is, quite literally, brighter and purer. As we discern more and more truths and as we radiate the corresponding spiritual light, that brightness brings awareness and understanding to situations we are faced with and lights the path we must trod (see Psalm 119:105).

Lasting Power of Discerned Spiritual Light

Coming to discern light brings about a closeness to God that is unmatched by what sensory signs can provide. Remember, the Holy Ghost, who is the testator of all truth, accompanies and could very well be the spiritual energy for our radiation of light. Receiving a witness of truth from the Holy Ghost is analogous to saying that we have come to discern and thus radiate spiritual light. I hope you have seen that special light as it newly radiates from a recent convert of the Church. There is something so pure and unfiltered about that light that is difficult to sense elsewhere.

The scriptures are replete with examples of the greater lasting power of conversion by the Spirit (i.e., discernment of spiritual light) rather than by signs and wonders. Perhaps the most prominent example is that of Laman and Lemuel, who had been visited by a rebuking angel more than once and had observed countless other manifestations of heavenly power in the form of tangible signs—earth shaking, a guiding ball (or compass) with changing messages, and so on. Yet, their repentance, no matter how meaningful it seemed (see 1 Nephi 16:4–5), never lasted long. In short, there never seemed to be an accompanying purification and thus no increase in discernment. At one point, Nephi reminds them of the missing element of their repentance, or conversion: "Ye are swift to do iniquity but slow to remember the Lord your God. Ye have *seen* an angel, and he spake unto you; yea, ye have *heard* his voice from time to time; and he hath spoken unto you in a still small voice, *but ye were past feeling*, that ye could not feel his words; wherefore, he has spoken unto you like unto the voice of thunder, which did cause the earth to shake as if it were to divide asunder" (1 Nephi 17:45; emphasis added).

The fact that Laman and Lemuel had seen and heard an angel did not make a sufficiently lasting impression on them. While they were first spoken to by "a still small voice," ultimately the angel had to resort to a "voice of thunder" because they couldn't, or really wouldn't, hear the voice of the Spirit (1 Nephi 17:45). Because they were not tuned in, and because they did not keep the truths they had been taught as a priority, they could not *feel* the angel's words. No angelic visits or voices could force Laman and Lemuel to *choose* to believe in the truths they were being taught. Without believing, they could not exercise the faith necessary to *feel* the newly discerned spiritual light infuse their souls.

I know that Laman and Lemuel's storied disobedience is of great familiarity to most readers. But have you ever thought about how important the lesson they teach us is regarding the insignificance of angelic visits for true conversion? I'm sure most of us think that if an angel were to visit us, then we would most definitely know the gospel is true without a shadow of a doubt. Yet, remember Laman and Lemuel. Their example of being past feeling is further validated by Alma the Younger's rebuke from an angel. Just as with Laman and Lemuel, the angelic rebuke to Alma came with a "voice of thunder" (and earth shaking) (Mosiah 27:11; Alma 36:7). Yet, unlike Laman and Lemuel, Alma chose to lower his barriers of unbelief and call upon the Lord, leading to his discernment of spiritual light (see Alma 36:18).

Remarkably, the most significant aspect of Alma the Younger's conversion is *not* the angelic visit or even the experiences he passed through in the days that followed. The most noteworthy aspect is revealed when Alma relates his conversion years later during his sermon to the people of Zarahemla in Alma 5:45: "And this is not all. Do ye not suppose that I know of these things myself? Behold, I testify unto you that I do know that these things whereof I have spoken are true. And how do ye suppose that I know of their surety?" What do you think Alma will say next? Wouldn't it be something like "because an angel appeared to me and told me it is true"? "The earth shook and trembled from the sound of his voice"? "I couldn't move for days and was ultimately delivered by the miraculous mercy of the Lord"? Nope; none of those. Instead, Alma says: "Behold, I say unto you they are made known unto me by the Holy Spirit of God. Behold, I have fasted and prayed many days that I might know these things of myself. And now I do know of myself that they are true; for the Lord God hath made them manifest unto me by his Holy Spirit; and this is the spirit of revelation which is in me" (Alma 5:46).

In spite of the angelic visit that he could *see* and the voice of thunder that he could *hear*, Alma cites fasting and prayer and the resulting manifestations from the Holy Ghost as the most concrete confirmations of his conversion. This is because the discernment of spiritual light, always fueled by a witness from the Holy Ghost, more powerfully affects the *entire soul* than any physical sensation, even if that sensation comes in the form of a visitor from heaven. President Joseph Fielding Smith summarized this concept well: "When a [person] has the manifestation from the Holy Ghost, it leaves an indelible impression on [the] soul, one that is not easily erased. It is Spirit speaking to spirit, and it comes with convincing force. A manifestation of an angel, or even of the Son of God himself, would impress the eye and mind, and eventually become dimmed, but the impressions of the Holy Ghost sink deeper into the soul and are more difficult to erase."[5]

When your soul has been illuminated and purified by the light of truth, a spiritual manifestation can remain forever with you. It will not fade like the memory of a singular event; rather, if fueled by the companionship of the Holy Ghost, the manifestation will continue to radiate from you and provide increased discernment of the world around you. President Smith also said that "through the Holy Ghost the truth is woven into the very fibre and sinews of the body so that it cannot be forgotten."[6] That truth is light, and the more light we discern, the brighter our knowledge and greater our influence on others will become until the "perfect day" (Doctrine and Covenants 50:24).

Light has the power to purify physically by the UVGI purification of water and spiritually by the "forsak[ing] [of] that evil one" (Doctrine and Covenants 93:37). There are many effects of spiritual purification; one of these is an increase in our discernment of spiritual light and, with it, coming to know truth connected to (i.e., revealed by) that light. In a world that grows increasingly darkened by sin and moral decay, we need more and more discernment of spiritual light to keep our paths bright and our footings sure. Just as Helen Keller expertly experienced the world by using feedback that excluded the typical sensory inputs of sight and sound, our abilities to discern light and truth because of our more purified hearts will enable us to navigate the growing darkness of the world.

As our discernment of light grows, our knowledge of gospel truths is strengthened. These truths, and the light associated with them, become a part of who we are in a way that cannot be taken from us. The world can revile and mock these truths, but their veracity remains entirely and unalterably ours for as long as we continue to embrace them. This concept is captured beautifully in the first two stanzas of a poem penned by the American poet Richard Watson Gilder. The poem is titled "Love and Death" and is featured in the quotation from Helen Keller in the heading of this chapter.

> Now, who can take from us what we have known—
> We that have looked into each other's eyes?
> Though lowering night should blacken all the skies,
> The day is ours, and what the day has shown.

What we have seen and been, hath this not grown
  Part of our very selves? We, made love-wise,
  What power shall slay our steadfast memories,
  And who shall take from us what is our own?[7]

Notes

1. Helen Keller and Anne Sullivan, *The Story of My Life* (New York: Grosset & Dunlap, 1905), 8.

2. Keller and Sullivan, *Story of My Life*, 7–8.

3. D. Todd Christofferson, "Abide in My Love," *Ensign*, November 2016, 50.

4. Keller and Sullivan, *Story of My Life*, 74–75.

5. Joseph Fielding Smith, *Answers to Gospel Questions* (Salt Lake City: Deseret Book, 1957), 2:151.

6. Joseph Fielding Smith, *Doctrines of Salvation* (Salt Lake City: Bookcraft, 1954–56), 1:48.

7. Richard Watson Gilder, *The Poems of Richard Watson Gilder* (Boston: Houghton Mifflin, 1908), 63.

8

"See Him as He Is"

Our climb up the path to perfection is aided by encouragement from the scriptures. They hold the promise that we shall, if faithful in all things, become like Deity. . . . Thus, our adoration of Jesus is best expressed by our emulation of Jesus.[1]

—President Russell M. Nelson

In my high school seminary class, we began each day with a devotional given by one of the students. The devotionals were generally a few minutes long and involved sharing a thought, scripture, story, or testimony. Some students went above and beyond with elaborate object lessons, while others scurried to the front of the class with a hastily (and often randomly) chosen scripture to share. I figure that over the course of my high school seminary experience I sat through more than six hundred of these devotionals. Isn't that incredible? I have rarely considered the tremendous daily strength I undoubtedly received by hearing my classmates bear witness of gospel truths.

While the influence of most of these devotionals blended in with the general spiritual lift seminary provided, there were a few that left very distinct and memorable impressions. Just imagine—it's more than twenty years later, and I still remember some of the three-minute-long devotionals shared by my seminary classmates. One such devotional was shared when we were studying in the book of Alma. The student read the following two verses from Alma's sermon that he had given throughout the cities and villages of the Nephites to "stir them up in remembrance of their duty" (Alma 4:19). You may know these verses well:

> And now behold, I ask of you, my brethren of the church, have ye spiritually been born of God? Have ye received his image in your countenances? Have ye experienced this mighty change in your hearts? . . .
>
> I say unto you, can ye look up to God at that day with a pure heart and clean hands? I say unto you, can you look up, having the image of God engraven upon your countenances? (Alma 5:14, 19)

After sharing these poetic verses from Alma's introspection-inspiring sermon, my seminary classmate held up a large print of the painting titled *Mickey's Self Portrait*, created by the Disney master illustrator Charles Boyer.[2] The juxtaposition of this painting with the abovementioned verses had a powerful effect on me. In the painting, which has also been produced as a figurine, Mickey Mouse is seated in front of an easel and a mirror. On the easel is a canvas on which Mickey is painting as he looks at his own reflection in the mirror, clearly suggesting he is making an effort to paint a self-portrait.

The intricacies of this painting reveal profound symbols of the artist's message. Obviously, Mickey Mouse is seeing his own reflection in the mirror; yet the self-portrait that he has actually fashioned is of his creator, Walt Disney. In the top left of the easel is a small sketch sheet where several sample portraits of Walt Disney have been sketched, showing that it was always planned for the portrait to look as it does. The nearly full trash bin at the bottom right gives further indication that much planning, many tries, some mistakes, and continual perseverance were needed to get the portrait just right. The iconic set of Mickey Mouse ears on top of the easel has the name *Walt* showing on the front, giving yet another indication of the depth of connection between creator and creation.

The message of my classmate from more than twenty years ago—and my message now—is that we should be striving to see the Savior, the Father of our salvation, in ourselves. It has been planned from the very beginning that we should become like him. This doesn't mean we will be sinless or perfect, but we can be *perfected* and see in ourselves his likeness and glory. How can we come to know a "master whom [we have] not served" (Mosiah 5:13)? We cannot. It is through our service and obedience to the Lord that we come to know him and emulate him, thus becoming like him to such a degree that when we sit at the proverbial easel to paint our portrait, we will "see him as he is" (1 John 3:2). Not surprisingly, the process of reaching this goal has a lot to do with light . . . and eyes.

Eyesight

Our bodies are able to accomplish a multitude of incredible tasks simultaneously. We breathe air and extract the oxygen filling our lungs. Our heart pumps blood to carry that oxygen throughout the body. We hear and interpret sounds and interact with the world in countless other ways, all while thousands of other processes carry on within us. In this mix of all that is happening in your body at this very moment, there is one process that is arguably of greatest complexity: vision. About 30 percent of the brain is devoted to visual processing, compared to 8 percent for touch and just 3 percent for hearing.[3]

Take a moment to look around you. What do you see? Furniture, people, perhaps some plants. Ok, now what sort of things do you *perceive*? If there is a person sitting across the room from you, then you perceive that he or she is some distance away rather than directly next to you. If there are flowers within your field of view, then you perceive their color, from the green stem to the red or pink or purple or yellow petals. If you are outside and it is a sunny day, then you can readily perceive where the sun is in the sky by the intensity (brightness) of light coming from its location and the resultant shadows that are cast. The point is that your eyes take in light to see things around you, but your retina, optic nerve, and brain work with the detailed properties of that light to interpret what you are seeing or perceiving.

Let's follow the path that light takes to generate your vision of the green leaves on a tree that we will assume is located within your field of view. First, light is emitted from the sun. These photons of light come in a wide range of energies, from very low to extremely high. In just over eight minutes, this light from the sun hits the earth's atmosphere, which (thankfully) filters out nearly all of the dangerous, high-energy photons. Some of the photons with energies that are visible to humans (which make up the color spectrum, from violet to red), make it all the way down to the tree. This light hits a leaf on the tree, which absorbs most of the photons and uses their energy to convert water and carbon dioxide into life-sustaining sustenance in a process we know as "photosynthesis." The leaf's photosynthesis process makes use of nearly all the photons with visible energies; however, there are some photons that either are not used (reflected) by the leaf or are generated from the leaf in this process. These photons will radiate from the leaf in a multitude of directions, one of which is the path from the leaf to your eye. The light that enters your eye through the pupil is focused by the lens and, finally, hits the retina at the back of your eye. The retina consists of 150 million rod and cone cells, which absorb the light and convert its energy into electrical impulses that travel from the optic nerve to the brain. The strength of the electrical impulse is directly related to the energy of the photon. In the case of the leaf, that energy is in the green portion of the spectrum (or there is a combination of blue and yellow photons that, when detected, yield green), so the brain interprets the leaf to be the color green.[4]

That extraordinary process for seeing the green leaf is happening *constantly*, and not just with one single object (the leaf), but with hundreds of objects within your field of view; all are reflecting or generating photons based on the light from the sun (or some other light source) that subsequently enters your eyes and is translated into your vision. The reasons why an object is a certain color (i.e., radiates photons of light of certain energies) are not universal. In most cases, it's a simple matter of photons with some energies being absorbed and those of other energies being reflected by the object. There are dozens of other possibilities for light emission other than reflection, including when an object is a certain color because it absorbs all of the photons and then uses some of their energy to generate new photons of a certain energy or color (i.e., photoluminescence).

In case you are questioning the directional nature of light, just consider what would happen if someone stood directly in your line of sight of the leaf: Would you still be able to see it? Of course not, because the person would be blocking the direct path between the leaf and you, and the light is not going to bend around them (there are some deeper aspects of quantum physics that govern the actual position of a photon in a given instant, including the path a photon would travel; for the discussion here we are generalizing the path of a photon to be in a beam of light made of many photons).[5] Think about if the leaf were actually a light source, such as a light bulb, and you were sitting in a dark room. In that case, the directionality of the light would be even more apparent since you would see how shadowed the person standing between you and the light source would be. If you happen to see rays of light shining around the person in this scenario, it is not because you are seeing photons that are not entering your eyes; rather, you see rays of light because some of the photons moving in the direction of those rays are scattering off of particles in the air and being redirected into the path that leads to your eyes.

Much could be discussed about the physiological processes that happen once light enters the pupils of our eyes. For the purposes of this chapter, we will discuss just one: focusing. In each of your eyes are ciliary muscles that hold the lenses in place. Since the lens plays an important role in helping to focus the light so that it can be properly detected at the retina, adjustments made to the lens will create an adjustment in focus. Such lens adjustments are made by the ciliary muscles. When the ciliary muscles relax, they pull on and flatten the lens, which brings objects that are far away into better focus. To focus on closer objects, the ciliary muscles contract, which thickens the lens and brings clarity to close-up objects. In a way, using our ciliary muscles is like tuning the lens on a camera to adjust the focus. You can test your ciliary muscles by simply focusing on an object far away, then changing your focus to something much closer (note how the faraway object becomes blurry). If you do this without shifting the position of your head or eyes, then the same photons are entering your eye, and the only change is how you focused those incoming photons with your ciliary muscles.

To highlight the effects of how our focus determines what we are able to see, let's try two brief experiments. First, try focusing on one word in the center of a line in this paragraph. You can choose any single word near the center. Now, with your focus on that one word, try to read the words at either end of the line without moving your eyes or changing your focus. It's actually quite difficult, isn't it? Most likely, the words at the ends of the line appear blurry. This represents the limitations of our peripheral vision.

The reality is, we choose what to focus on and then rely rather heavily on our brains to fill in the details of what surrounds that object or area of focus. How the brain does this is quite complex but is certainly based on its experience. For instance, if you were to repeat the experiment above on a paragraph written in a language that you are not literate in, then the result would be even more blurriness to the words at the ends of the line.

The second experiment to demonstrate the effects of our focus is to count the number of black dots in the image in figure 8.1. You may recall this image from when it took the internet by storm in 2016, causing great

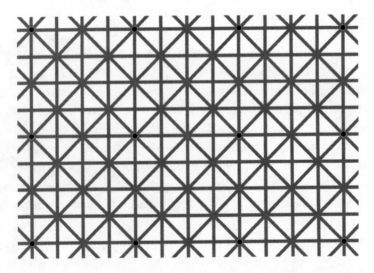

Figure 8.1. How many black dots are there in the image? The answer is twelve, but can you see them all at once? (See image at https://theverge.com/2016/9/12/12885574 /optical-illusion-12-black-dots and spiritualphysicsoflight.com.)

confusion as to why it appears to have black dots that move around as you shift your focus. Take a moment to test your ability to count the black dots. Did you count all twelve? If so, it's unlikely you saw them all at once. The reason is that your eyes are focusing only on one part of the image, likely where just one of the black dots is present and thus visible. Then, based on the fact that you can see the repetitive pattern of gray lines on a white background, your brain fills in the rest of the out-of-focus image with more of that same gray-line pattern, excluding the black dots that appear to be anomalies. In this way, even though you consciously may be aware of something (e.g., that there are twelve black dots in this image), it still won't change how your brain is able to perceive it. This has rather powerful connections to how we embrace and come to know truth, even when our temporal mind may not be able to fully comprehend or grasp it.

Ultimately, the processes that enable our eyesight are many and complex—from the source of the photons to how they interact with objects, to the photons from those objects that subsequently enter our eyes, and finally to how our eyes detect information from those photons and interpret their data into vision. There are likely hundreds of correlations to spiritual light amid these processes; you may have already come up with some as you read this section. Of most relevance for the remainder of this chapter is the parallel between how our physical eyes focus and how our spiritual eyes focus, which leads to the interpretation and perception of the physical and spiritual light that is around us; in other words, our focus determines what we see.

God Is Light

Before diving into how we focus spiritual eyes, let's review some of the other properties of light that we have covered. Over the course of this book, we have established a foundational understanding of light and some of its spiritual implications. We all radiate light, sense light, and through righteous living, come to discern light. Untold amounts of information are able to be transported because of light. Light is also a physically formidable force with the ability to burn and even move things that are not able to withstand its power. Now we will bring together the spiritual discernment of light and the physical power of light to show how coming closer to God truly makes us more like him and thus prepares us to be in his presence.

Since the overarching goal of our mortal journey is to become like God, let's flesh out the details of this goal by beginning with a verse that explains something very important that we know about God: "This then is the message which we have heard of him, and declare unto you, that God is light, and in him is no darkness at all" (1 John 1:5).

While latter-day revelation has brought clarity to the physical nature of God, that he "has a body of flesh and bones as tangible as man's" (Doctrine and Covenants 130:22), it is yet worth considering how literal John's declaration of "God is light" is intended to be. In an insightful article titled "How 'God Is Light,'" Daniel Peterson points out that the connection between light and God is a teaching held by numerous religions and is found in the Jewish Dead Sea Scrolls, in the beliefs of Zoroastrianism, and in the "Light Verse," a verse from the Quran, the Islamic holy book.[6]

Upon reading Peterson's article, I asked a friend of mine, who is Muslim, about the "Light Verse," since we often have insightful and inspiring theological conversations. He confirmed that the passage is indeed quite famous and comes from a chapter titled "An-Nur," which means "the light" in Arabic. He pointed out that there is only one official version of the Quran, which is in Arabic, so the translation to English varies—something we are also quite familiar with when it comes to the Holy Bible, which we believe "to be the word of God as far as it is translated correctly" (Articles of Faith 1:8). The translation he pointed me to (the Sahih International version) presents the verse, Quran 24:35, as follows: "[God] is the Light of the heavens and the earth. The example of His light is like a niche within which is a lamp, the lamp is within glass, the glass as if it were a pearly [white] star lit from [the oil of] a blessed olive tree, neither of the east nor of the west, whose oil would almost glow even if untouched by fire. Light upon light. [God] guides to His light whom He wills. And [God] presents examples for the people, and [God] is Knowing of all things."[7]

This verse from the Islamic holy book led Abu Hamid Muhammad al-Ghazali, who is noted by Peterson to be "one of the greatest thinkers and writers in the Islamic tradition," to write a treatise called "The Niche of Lights." Peterson goes on to explain that in the end, al-Ghazali argues that calling God "light" is no mere metaphor, but that, rather, our earthly light is a dim foretaste of God, who deserves the word "light" more than any fire or light bulb or star or sun that our mortal eyes can see: "It will be unveiled to you," [al-Ghazali] writes, "that God is the highest and farthest light, and . . . that He is the real, true light—He alone, without any partner in that."

His argument is a clever one, and one that religious believers beyond the world of Islam might well appreciate. I cannot summarize it here, but I can offer a hint: Light, al-Ghazali contends, is both something we can see but also something that allows us to see other things. But light's capacity to illuminate other things is limited, and sight can be hindered by obstacles and other interferences. Reason, however, can consider things—can "see" things—that are beyond the power of our vision because they are too small, or too far away, or blocked from our sight by any number of other factors. Accordingly, reason deserves to be called "light" even more than the familiar optical phenomenon does. And, so, onward and upward to God.[8]

An English translation of "The Niche of Light" was produced by David Buchman in 1998, and Peterson's article led me to study this compelling work. The depth with which al-Ghazali explores the "degrees of light" and how God is "the highest and farthest light" is incredible. I found that the heading of the first chapter of the treatise nicely summed up the literal connection between God and light: "Clarifying that the real light is God and that the name 'light' for everything else is sheer metaphor, without reality."[9] Could the connection become any more literal than that?

No matter how detailed our analysis of the physical and spiritual physics of light may become, they will never supersede nor indeed be able to comprehend the true reality of all that light actually is, which is above all fully embodied by God, the "Father of lights" (Doctrine and Covenants 67:9). No matter what we do with light, how we study or manipulate it, define or interpret it, the reality that the ultimate source is God and that his all-encompassing light brings with it a knowledge, perception, understanding, and, in short, omniscience is a doctrine that appears consistently across major religions.

Note that it was not stated that God is *only* light, in a way that would discount his substance and physicality. In fact, the verse from 1 John confirms this by noting that God is light *and* "in him is no darkness at all," suggesting that he is of real substance so that he can physically contain something within (a niche, if you will) and that this something is "no darkness at all" (1 John 1:5).

Eye Single to the Glory of God

The true understanding and use of light, to its fullest, is wholly held by God. The actual use of light by God, who is light, completely dwarfs all that we have determined about light in our finite, mortal state. With this in mind, let's now turn back to the subject of how we are to become like God. If God is light, then it is a rather straightforward conclusion to say that "that which is *of* God is light" (Doctrine and Covenants 50:24; emphasis added). Therefore, in one sense, to become like God would be to also be full of light and have no darkness at all.

How do we become full of light? And, what does this actually imply? In answer to the first of these queries, the scriptures contain a very specific doctrine. This is one of the rare teachings that is repeated almost word-for-word in the New Testament (twice), Book of Mormon, and Doctrine and Covenants:

> The light of the body is the eye: therefore when thine eye is single, thy whole body also is full of light; but when thine eye is evil, thy body also is full of darkness. (Luke 11:34)

> The light of the body is the eye; if, therefore, thine eye be single, thy whole body shall be full of light. (3 Nephi 13:22; see Matthew 6:22)

> And if your eye be single to my glory, your whole bodies shall be filled with light, and there shall be no darkness in you; and that body which is filled with light comprehendeth all things. (Doctrine and Covenants 88:67)

What does it mean to have your eye single to the glory of God? During a time when I was pondering this question deeply, I posed it to members of the Gospel Doctrine class that I was teaching in my ward. To be honest, when I asked them the question I felt like I had already arrived at a fairly solid answer and supposed my role would be to help lead them to said answer. However, they would prove me wrong. Their answers were elaborate and varied and wonderful. From examples of sacrifice to testimonies of faith and obedience, I came to realize that there is great individuality in what it means to have an eye single to the glory of God. There was, nevertheless, one common theme among the answers: having an eye single to the glory of God starts with *focusing* on God.

Based on the experience with my Gospel Doctrine class, I will not attempt to provide a definitive interpretation here. Instead, allow me to point out just a few of the many interesting perspectives on what it means to have an eye single to God's glory. To start, I find President Russell M. Nelson's prophetic counsel on the topic of *Israel* meaning "let God prevail" to be consistent with having our eye be single; consider his probing questions on this topic:

> Are *you* willing to let God prevail in your life? Are *you* willing to let God be the most important influence in your life? Will you allow His words, His commandments, and His covenants to influence what you do each day? Will you allow His voice to take priority over any other? Are you *willing* to let whatever He needs you to do take precedence over every other ambition? Are you *willing* to have your will swallowed up in His?[10]

The Light of the Body Is the Eye

It's clear that our physical eyes, because of eyesight, provide the most powerful evidence of the presence or absence of visible light. Yet eyesight is based on light coming into the eyes—not light emitting from them. The Savior's teaching that the "light of the body is the eye" (Luke 11:34) seems to suggest that something about the eye is connected to the light that is within (or that, perhaps, even comes from) the body.

To some, the meaning of this phrase is interpreted as the spiritual brightness that can often be detected by looking into a person's eyes. A well-known example of this would be the comment (referenced earlier in this book) from a governmental representative in Israel who, upon acknowledging the Church's commitment not to have BYU students proselyte in Israel, quipped, "What are you going to do about the light that is in their eyes?" Upon sharing this story, President James E. Faust proceeded to teach the following:

> What was that light in their eyes which was so obvious to our friend? The Lord Himself gives the answer: "And the light which shineth, which giveth you light, is through him who enlighteneth your eyes, which is the same light that quickeneth your understandings" [Doctrine and Covenants 88:11]. Where did that light come from? Again the Lord gives the answer: "I am the true light that lighteth every man that cometh into the world" [Doctrine and Covenants 93:2]. The Lord is the true light, "and the Spirit enlighteneth every man through the world, that hearkeneth to the voice of the Spirit" [Doctrine and Covenants 84:46]. This light shows in our countenances as well as in our eyes.[11]

In addition to being a detectable light in the eyes of the faithful, there is another perspective on the light of the body being the eye. Think about the metaphorical significance of the eye in terms of our focus and motivation in life. This is partly related to what is called our "mind's eye," which represents our ability to see things with our mind. Yet, even beyond the conjured scenes made visible in the mind, there is an aspect of our internal eye (perhaps it is even the eyes of our spirit) that indicates our true focus, motivations, intentions, and so forth. I believe it is the focusing of this spiritual eye that distinguishes things like service from charity—the act is the same but the intent is entirely different. In short, the focus of the spiritual eye is the why behind all that we do.

A scriptural connection to this internal or spiritual eye is found in something referred to as the "eye of faith" by Alma and Moroni. The eye of faith is our portal to God, linking our acts of obedience with our uttermost desire to serve, be like, and be with God. I suggest this goes hand in hand with having pure intent and righteous motivation behind our obedience. Note the following teachings on this topic by Alma and Moroni, respectively:

Do ye exercise faith in the redemption of him who created you? Do you *look forward with an eye of faith*, and view this mortal body raised in immortality, and this corruption raised in incorruption, to stand before God to be judged according to the deeds which have been done in the mortal body? (Alma 5:15; emphasis added)

And there were many whose faith was so exceedingly strong, even before Christ came, who could not be kept from within the veil, but truly *saw with their eyes the things which they had beheld with an eye of faith*, and they were glad. (Ether 12:19; emphasis added)

The more firmly we plant ourselves in gospel standards and obedience to God's commandments, the more wholly our spiritual eyes (the eye of faith) become focused and set on the Lord and his purposes. We become less subject to the distractions of the world and more sensitive to the promptings of the Spirit. This spiritual firmness is a key aspect of the strengthened bond between spirit and body and is the reason the light of the body is this spiritual eye—without its focus on the Lord, our righteousness "profiteth [us] nothing" (1 Corinthians 13:3). We see this critical combination set forth throughout the scriptures: the Lord requires "the heart and a willing mind" (Doctrine and Covenants 64:34; see Mosiah 7:33). King David explains this combination to his son, Solomon:

And thou, Solomon my son, know thou the God of thy father, and serve him with a perfect heart and with a willing mind: for the Lord searcheth all hearts, and *understandeth all the imaginations of the thoughts*: if thou seek him, he will be found of thee; but if thou forsake him, he will cast thee off for ever. (1 Chronicles 28:9; emphasis added)

To conclude our consideration of the light of the body being the eye, and that this can be considered to be a spiritual eye that is the focus and motivation behind all that we do, consider the glorious promise given by the Lord in the Doctrine and Covenants. After declaring that the light of the body is the eye, the Lord makes a transition from "eye single to God" to "mind single to God," providing further substantiation to this correlation:

And if your *eye be single to my glory*, your whole bodies shall be filled with light, and there shall be no darkness in you; and that body which is filled with light comprehendeth all things.

Therefore, sanctify yourselves that your *minds become single to God*, and the days will come that *you shall see him*; for he will unveil his face unto you, and it shall be in his own time, and in his own way, and according to his own will. (Doctrine and Covenants 88:67–68; emphasis added)

While serving as president of Brigham Young University—Idaho, Kim B. Clark gave a devotional on the topic of always remembering Christ. In the devotional, President Clark discussed what he called the "mirror of Christ" as being the mirror we should look into for guidance and direction, rather than the "mirror of the world":

We see ourselves in the mirror of Christ as He sees us, and we see our actions and our behavior as He sees them and as He would have them be. We see Him as He really is; and we, therefore, see ourselves as we might really become. Moreover, as we act on what we see, as our deep remembering moves us to do what is right, we become more like Him.[12]

Comprehendeth All Things

As quoted above, the "body which is filled with light comprehendeth all things" (Doctrine and Covenants 88:67). The link between this doctrine and what it means to have an eye single to the glory of God makes me think of an experience with my daughter, Ellie, when she was in preschool. Ellie was a fairly talkative three-year-old and would unleash a flood of wonderfully hilarious stories just after she was picked up each day. On one occasion, my wife and I were asking Ellie about her day, and she rehearsed a story that, to the best of our interpretation, involved most of the children not paying attention in class. At one point I asked her, "What did your teacher say?" She then did her best serious face and, while tapping her finger right in between her eyes, slowly and deliberately said, "Keep your eyes on the teacher!"

Where we are looking has a significant influence on what we are learning. Having our eyes trained on something other than what we are supposed to be paying attention to will greatly hamper how much we learn. Conversely, having our eyes fixed on the source of information we are seeking to acquire greatly enhances our learning. I see validation of this truth regularly as a college professor. In courses where lectures are given entirely from the chalkboard, students must look up to see what is being written or referred to. However, when the same material is taught from a slide presentation that all students have been given in advance, then they rarely look up from their desks. The average performance of students in the chalkboard-taught classes is consistently better than that of students who barely glance up at previously viewed slide presentations.

So it is with the gospel. Having our eyes trained and focused on the Lord is the surest way that we can learn eternal truths. What it means to look continuously to the Lord can be discovered through the following three scriptural examples:

> Let us lay aside every weight, and the sin which doth so easily beset us, and let us run with patience the race that is set before us,
>
> Looking unto Jesus the author and finisher of our faith; who for the joy that was set before him endured the cross, despising the shame, and is set down at the right hand of the throne of God. (Hebrews 12:1–2)

> Look unto God with firmness of mind, and pray unto him with exceeding faith, and he will console you in your afflictions, and he will plead your cause, and send down justice upon those who seek your destruction. (Jacob 3:1)

> And now, my son, I trust that I shall have great joy in you, because of your steadiness and your faithfulness unto God; for as you have commenced in your youth to look to the Lord your God, even so I hope that you will continue in keeping his commandments; for blessed is he that endureth to the end. (Alma 38:2)

On the flip side, there are certainly warnings to those who do not keep their eyes upon the Lord, as shown by Jacob in ancient scripture and by Elder Quentin L. Cook in modern-day revelation:

Wherefore, because of their blindness, which blindness came by looking beyond the mark, they must needs fall; for God hath taken away his
plainness from them, and delivered unto them many things which they
cannot understand, because they desired it. And because they desired
it God hath done it, that they may stumble. (Jacob 4:14)

Today there is a tendency among some of us to "look beyond the
mark" rather than to maintain a testimony of gospel basics. We do this
when we substitute the philosophies of men for gospel truths, engage
in gospel extremism, seek heroic gestures at the expense of daily con-
secration, or elevate rules over doctrine. Avoiding these behaviors
will help us avoid the theological blindness and stumbling that Jacob
described. . . .

When we look beyond the mark, we are looking beyond Christ,
the only name under heaven whereby we might be saved.[13]

Finally, there are promises that looking to God will lead to our bodies
being filled with light. These promises imply that obedience to the commandments is necessary, even through trial and difficulty. Because light is
truth and truth is knowledge (see Doctrine and Covenants 84:45; 93:28), a
body that is filled with light will indeed comprehend all things. As President Spencer W. Kimball taught:

I have learned that where there is a prayerful heart, a hungering after
righteousness, a forsaking of sins, and [an] obedience to the commandments of God, the Lord pours out more and more light until there
is finally power to pierce the heavenly veil and to know more than
[humanity] knows. A person of such righteousness has the priceless
promise that one day [he or she] shall see the Lord's face and know that
he is (see D&C 93:1).[14]

All Things Shall Be Done according to Thy Word

Among the many incredible prophets throughout the Book of Mormon,
the prophet Nephi, son of Helaman, has always stood out to me. Like
his great-grandfather, Alma the Younger, Nephi dedicated his life to the
preaching of God's word (see Helaman 5:1–4), yet his extensive labors

were mostly met with rejection because the people were "in a state of such awful wickedness" (Helaman 7:4). Even still, Nephi did experience some success. This included the miraculous events that occurred when he was imprisoned with his brother, Lehi, as they were preaching among the Lamanites. That scene involved a fantastic display of light, from shining faces to pillars of bright fire (see Helaman 5:22–50).

There is something truly remarkable about Nephi that comes about during his preaching to the people in Zarahemla. During one particularly long day, he prayed and preached from his garden tower, prophesied the death of the chief judge, was accused of the judge's murder, and then was released after identifying the actual culprit—what a day! After this series of events, Nephi was on his way home and was pondering everything that had happened when the voice of the Lord came to him and declared:

> Blessed art thou, Nephi, for those things which thou hast done; for I have beheld how thou hast with unwearyingness declared the word, which I have given unto thee, unto this people. And thou hast not feared them, and *hast not sought thine own life, but hast sought my will, and to keep my commandments.*
>
> And now, because thou hast done this with such unwearyingness, behold, I will bless thee forever; and I will make thee mighty in word and in deed, in faith and in works; yea, even that *all things shall be done unto thee according to thy word, for thou shalt not ask that which is contrary to my will.* (Helaman 10:4–5; emphasis added)

All of the Lord's words to Nephi are touching and inspiring; but most pertinent to our present discussion is the promise that "all things [should] be done" according to Nephi's word (Helaman 10:5). How is it that God could put so very much trust in one person? The answer is found in what the Lord said before and after this promise: Nephi's will was swallowed up in the Lord's will, such that Nephi would not ask for anything contrary to it.

Nephi had sought the Lord's will to such a degree that Nephi considered his own life secondary to keeping God's commandments. It wasn't that the Lord was granting Nephi something that he had earned—namely, that he could ask anything and it would be done *because* he'd done all of these things. No, the reality is that by so fully having his eye single to the glory of God, even with "unwearyingness," Nephi had reached a spiritual state wherein he simply would "not ask that which is contrary to [God's] will" (Helaman 10:5). As Elder David A. Bednar taught:

> We come to know the Savior as we do our best to go where He wants us to go, as we strive to say what He wants us to say, and as we become what He wants us to become. As we submissively acknowledge our total dependence upon Him, He enlarges our capacity to serve ever more effectively. Gradually, our desires align more completely with His desires, and His purposes become our purposes, such that we would "not ask that which is contrary to [His] will."
>
> Serving Him requires all of our heart, might, mind, and strength. Consequently, selflessly serving others counteracts the self-centered and selfish tendencies of the natural man.[15]

Our most complete spiritual transformation occurs when our will is fully swallowed up in the will of the Father, as the Savior's will so perfectly was in *all* things (see Mosiah 15:7). Because Nephi's life was filled with decisions that put God first, no matter the cost, he had reached a point of perfect alignment between his will and God's will. That produces a body filled with light, so much so that Nephi comprehended all things and would not ask for anything that would be amiss.

Growing Brighter and Brighter

The example of Nephi demonstrates an ultimate goal for having our eye single to the glory of God and, thus, our bodies filled with light. Yet, most of us will spend our lifetimes striving for, but not necessarily reaching, this level of absolute submission to the Lord's will. The good news is that the Lord always knew it would be a process. One righteous decision at a time, we come to discern greater light—light that fills our bodies more and more, brighter and brighter. This is all brought together in the words of the Savior to the Prophet Joseph Smith:

> That which is of God is light; and he that receiveth light, and continueth in God, receiveth more light; and that light groweth brighter and brighter until the perfect day.

And again, verily I say unto you, and I say it that you may know the truth, that you may chase darkness from among you. (Doctrine and Covenants 50:24–25)

Our brightening light corresponds to knowing more truth as we chase away darkness, doubt, and uncertainty. As our light grows brighter, we become ever more like our Savior, the father of our salvation, even he who is the source of all light. Someday soon, that Light will return in great glory to the earth, as has been prophesied for millennia. When Christ returns, all the earth will be exposed to his glorious light. As we discussed in chapter 6, exposure to such an unimaginable brightness of light will have a consuming, destructive effect on all who have not come to discern that light for themselves. Meanwhile, for those who are prepared, whose light has grown brighter and brighter, what appears will not be a blinding, destructive, painful power but a warm, welcome, and familiar light.

We may not be able to fully capture how this all will happen at the Lord's Second Coming, but there is something we can know for certain: if we are prepared, what we see coming from the East will be familiar, since it will be the very reflection of our own countenance:

Beloved, now are we the sons of God, and it doth not yet appear what we shall be: but we know that, when he shall appear, *we shall be like him*; for *we shall see him as he is*. (1 John 3:2; emphasis added)

It is those who are able to see the Savior at his coming that will become like him. I don't believe this means that these people have attained perfection, just as (from the analogy that began this chapter) Mickey Mouse is not the embodiment of Walt Disney in every last respect. Yet, those who are ever striving to do good, to resist all temptations, to serve in spite of all obstacles; in short, those who are doing all they can to have their eye single to the glory of God will be filled with light *at that day*. It's not necessarily *before* he appears, but it's *when* he appears that we shall be like him and shall thus be *filled* with light.

. Notes

1. Russell M. Nelson, "Perfection Pending," *Ensign*, November 1995, 86–87.

2. Note that Boyer's work was modeled after Norman Rockwell's piece *Triple Self Portrait* and was first created as *Walt's Self Portrait* with Walt Disney looking in the mirror and the actual sketch being of Mickey Mouse. The version referred to here, *Mickey's Self Portrait*, was created by Boyer a few years later; see https://your wdwstore.net/_p_67482.html. See also Jim Korkis, "The Norman Rockwell-Walt Disney Connection," *Mouse Planet*, https://mouseplanet.com/9631/The _Norman_RockwellWalt_Disney_Connection.

3. D. Grady, "The Vision Thing: Mainly in the Brain," *Discover Magazine*, June 1993, http://discovermagazine.com/1993/jun/thevisionthingma227.

4. After having written this thought experiment, I discovered that the concept of photons leaving the sun, hitting a leaf, and then entering a person's eye is actually a rather hotly debated scientific query. It's not an issue of whether light from the sun provides photons that ultimately allow us to see; rather, it is a debate about the processes from emission at the sun to entering the eye. For those interested, one such thread of discussion on this topic can be found here: https://quora.com/A-photon-leaves-the-sun-hits-a-leaf-hits-my-retina-Is-the -photon-that-hit-my-retina-exactly-the-same-photon-from-the-Sun.

5. One of the most perplexing, yet fundamental, aspects of quantum mechanics is the uncertainty principle, which relates to the position and momentum of a quantum particle (e.g., a photon of light). Basically, the wave nature of photons means that their precise position is probabilistically spread out in space and does not become fixed or known until the photon interacts with something. The best illustration of this is through the famous double-slit experiment, which shows that when a single photon passes through a plate with a double slit, its behavior is influenced by both slits, resulting in a wavelike interference pattern. This is observed by tracking where the single photon's momentum is transferred to on a detector screen on the other side of the plate with the double slit and repeating this for many subsequent single photons, one at a time. The net effect results in a distinct interference pattern on the screen. For a useful scientific study with supporting videos on this, see Reuben S. Aspden and Miles J. Padgett, "Video recording true single-photon double-slit interference," *American Journal of Physics* 84 (August 2016): 671. For a less scientifically detailed but still very helpful discussion, see Avery Thompson, "The Logic-Defying Double-Slit

Experiment Is Even Weirder Than You Thought," *Popular Mechanics*, August 2016: https://popularmechanics.com/science/a22280/double-slit-experiment -even-weirder. See also Jay Bennett, "The Double-Slit Experiment That Blew Open Quantum Mechanics," *Popular Mechanics*, July 2016: https://popular mechanics.com/science/a22094/video-explainer-double-slit-experiment. Note that for the purpose of discussions in this chapter (and through the majority of this book), focus is on beams of light (many photons), which take on a more deterministic behavior in terms of position, especially when observed at the macroscale (e.g., a laser beam). One additional consideration worth noting is that there are situations where gravity is able to bend the path of light (known as "gravitational lensing"), which was part of Einstein's general theory of relativity. However, this is only observed with massive gravitational fields such as those observed in astronomical bodies (e.g., galaxies) and thus does not have relevance to our simple example of light traveling between a leaf and an observer.

6. Daniel Peterson, "How 'God Is Light,'" *Deseret News*, January 2020. https:// deseret.com/faith/2020/1/30/21080990/daniel-peterson-how-god-is-light -dead-sea-scrolls-john-quran-islam-al-ghazalithe-niche-of-lights.

7. See translation at https://quran.com/24/35?translations=31,43,102,101,84,22 ,21,85,20,19,17,18,95; brackets in original.

8. Peterson, "How 'God Is Light.'"

9. Al-Ghazali, *The Niche of Lights*, trans. David Buchman (Provo, UT: Brigham Young University Press, 1998).

10. Russell M. Nelson, "Let God Prevail," *Ensign*, November 2020, 94; emphasis in original.

11. James E. Faust, "The Light in Their Eyes," *Ensign*, November 2005, 20.

12. Kim B. Clark, "That Ye Do Always Remember Him," *Brigham Young University— Idaho Education Week Devotional*, June 2006, https://byui.edu/Presentations /transcripts/devotionals/2006_06_29_clark.htm.

13. Quentin L. Cook, "Looking beyond the Mark," *Ensign*, March 2003, 42, 44.

14. Spencer W. Kimball, "Give the Lord Your Loyalty," *Ensign*, March 1980, 4.

15. David A. Bednar, "If Ye Had Known Me," *Ensign*, November 2016, 102.

9

"Light of the World"

I bear witness that darkness cannot stand before the brilliant light of the Son of the living God! . . . Even after the darkest night, the Savior of the world will lead you to a gradual, sweet, and bright dawn that will assuredly rise within you.[1]

—Elder Dieter F. Uchtdorf

The scientific world remains filled with unknowns. In the United States, more than 54,000 doctorate degrees were awarded in science and engineering fields in 2016.[2] Just imagine, 54,000 multiyear, inquisitive, scientific studies addressing unanswered questions. That is a lot of discovery! If each degree took an average of six years to earn, then this amounts to more than 320,000 person years of research, and this is only within the United States; globally, this number of research hours stretches to the millions.

Despite this expanse of scientific study, there remains so much yet to be understood, discovered, or developed. One prominent example in physics is the absence of a Grand Unified Theory, or Theory of Everything,[3] which would be a single explanation of all constants, forces, and interactions in the universe. Between the mysterious gravitational force and strange behaviors of subatomic particles, developing a theory that can explain these (and other) phenomena without contradicting existing knowledge remains one of the loftiest scientific goals.

In the face of all that is unknown in the scientific world, there is the gospel of Jesus Christ with its eternal truths. The gospel is distinct because it operates in reverse in terms of finding truth and how truth relates to a unified model. While scientists, from Plato and Copernicus to Einstein and Hawking, have worked from discovery to discovery toward a unified model of the universe, the Architect of the universe provided us with knowledge of what unifies all truth from the very beginning—the plan of salvation and the central role of our Savior Jesus Christ. How lasting are scientific constants? How consistent are scientific theories when applied across all time and all space? No one can know. Meanwhile, the Atonement of Christ the Lord and the truths extending therefrom are unbound by time and unmatched in influence or power. Indeed, his Atonement is *infinite*, his truths are *eternal*, and his paths are straight. All that surrounds us in this universe is part of the Father's plan for the salvation of his children—the grandest unified *reality* of all.

What we learn scientifically should be kept in perspective with the truths of the gospel, not the other way around. In this book, we have explored how the physics of spiritual light may correlate with the scientific explanations and observations of physical light. Yet, undergirding all of this discussion should be the foundational truths of the Father's plan of salvation and the Atonement of Jesus Christ. It is Jesus who bears the title "light of the world" (John 9:5) and is the one by whom "the worlds are and were created" (Doctrine and Covenants 76:24). He is the Grand Scientist of the Universe, with the truths to unify and reconcile all that we know with all that we do not. In this final chapter, the focus will be on the spiritual implications of light and the role of Jesus Christ in the operation of spiritual light. Using a story of miraculous healing from the New Testament, we will explore some of the most prominent scriptural teachings about light and its role in our path to the Savior. This is the culmination of how we see, feel, and know truth, since "whatsoever is truth is light" (Doctrine and Covenants 84:45).

The Light of the World

Have you ever pondered on what it will be like to meet the Savior? What setting do you picture at this thought? Will you embrace him or fall at his feet? Perhaps if one hundred people were asked these questions there would be one hundred different scenes painted of that reunion. For me, when I close my eyes, clear the canvas of my mind, and conjure an image of Christ, it is nearly always the same: a white robe, glorious brightness shining all around, a smiling face, and always, always outstretched arms.[4] The scriptures are replete with imagery related to the Lord's "arms of mercy" (Mosiah 16:12 and Alma 5:33) being extended toward us—a gesture that signifies Christ's great, inviting love for his children.

We are given numerous examples in the scriptures of meetings others have had with the Savior. These span from visions of his premortal spirit to meetings during his mortal ministry and, finally, to visitations from the resurrected Christ. There's the brother of Jared's faith-prompted vision of the premortal Jesus (see Ether 3:6–13), Peter and the sons of Zebedee being called by the Master to leave their nets and follow him (see Matthew 4:18–22), and Mary Magdalene's tender visit from the resurrected Lord at his empty tomb (see John 20:11–18). Thinking of ourselves in similar situations can help with visualizing our own personal reunion with the Master.

There is one particular meeting that has always especially touched me. As recorded in John 9, it is the story of a man that was blind from birth and who, on the Sabbath day, is healed by Jesus. Of all the miracles and magnificent experiences that happened in the Savior's mortal ministry, this particular encounter has several unique aspects. First, it is rare for a single story to encompass an entire chapter in one of the Gospels; yet, this specific healing experience takes up the entire 9th chapter of John. Key doctrines are taught or implied, including the reality of premortal existence, confirmation of agency, and clarification of proper worship on the Sabbath day. Yet it's not just these distinctive qualities and doctrinal teachings that make this story so compelling; rather, it is the touching faith and courage of the healed man leading up to his meeting with Christ at the end of the chapter.

Immediately prior to healing the blind man, Jesus taught his disciples, "As long as I am in the world, *I am the light of the world*" (John 9:5; emphasis added). He then anointed the eyes of the man with clay and instructed him to wash in the pool of Siloam. The man followed the Lord's instructions and was healed. What followed for this man provides a type for many of the experiences we may have in our lives once we choose to embrace the Lord's light.

Before we explore what transpired after the healing of the blind man, I'd like to first delve deeper into the Savior's teaching that he is "the light of the world" (John 9:5). Throughout this book, we have examined how light interacts with our souls, how it is radiated and sensed, and how spiritual light can be discerned through believing and exercising faith. In all, the source of that light has been indicated as the Light of Christ. What *is* the Light of Christ? How is the Light of Christ related to Christ himself? What is the ultimate purpose of light?

The Source of All Light

As we've discussed, all forms of energy must have a source. This scientific law of the universe is well supported by our belief that you cannot create something from nothing (often termed *ex nihilo*, which is Latin for "out of nothing") and that all things come from previously existing constituents. Hence, light is generated from some source. This is also related to the fact that light is a wave, which means it is always in motion. Waves cannot be stored, whether they are of light, ocean water, sound, or anything else.

When considering spiritual light, this scientific reality—that *light cannot be stored*—becomes of great significance. Since light must be generated from a source, even spiritual light that radiates from (and is within) us must come from a light source. That source, whether it be within us or at some place at the center of the universe, is the Light of Christ.

Jesus declared, "I am the true light that lighteth every man that cometh into the world" (Doctrine and Covenants 93:2). Often the importance of the Light of Christ is oversimplified when this unseen power is defined as a person's conscience. While there is scriptural support that the Light of Christ aids us in the determination of right versus wrong, it is also clear that such light is intended to lead one to the gospel, wherein the more constant guidance from the Holy Ghost can be obtained.

The importance and power of the Light of Christ extend *far* beyond one's conscience, even when that conscience is amplified by the Holy Ghost, fueling greater brightness from the Light of Christ. Consider the following insights regarding the immense scope of the Light of Christ:

> He that ascended up on high, as also he descended below all things, in that he comprehended all things, that he might be in all and through all things, the light of truth.
>
> Which truth shineth. This is the light of Christ. As also he is in the sun, and the light of the sun, and the power thereof by which it was made. . . .
>
> The light which is in all things, which giveth life to all things, which is the law by which all things are governed, even the power of God who sitteth upon his throne, who is in the bosom of eternity, who is in the midst of all things. (Doctrine and Covenants 88:6–7, 13)

These few verses of doctrine, revealed to the Prophet Joseph Smith, remind us of how very little we grasp about the Light of Christ. The shining of Christ's perfect comprehension emanates from the same source as the light of the sun *and* the power by which the sun was made. To envision the immensity of this power, consider that the sun emits enough energy (via light) to warm the entire earth even from 93 million miles away. Beyond heat, there is also electrical energy (electricity) that can be generated by converting sunlight energy using solar panels or solar heat plants. Based on electricity usage around the world in the year 2014, the earth is exposed to enough light from the sun in a single day to power the entire globe for more than twenty years. Of course, this would require a means of capturing and storing such energy—a subject of great scientific interest and active research—but imagine the magnitude of energy that is coming from the sun to be able to provide such intense capability in a single day and from 93 million miles away! Now remember that the power by which the source of such solar energy was created is the Light of Christ, "even the power of God who sitteth upon his throne" (Doctrine and Covenants 88:13).

What's more, the Light of Christ is also giving "life to all things" (Doctrine and Covenants 88:13). Perhaps this is referring to the fact that nothing on Earth could survive without the light of the sun,[5] which we just learned is also part of the Light of Christ. Or, perhaps it is even more than that—some other life-sustaining force that we have no ability to scientifically measure. No matter what, it is clear that the Light of Christ is far more than just the conscience of human beings that gives promptings for that which is right, though it is that as well (see Moroni 7:12–19). The Guide to the Scriptures, available at churchofjesuschrist.org, provides a nice summary and includes nearly comprehensive documentation to scriptures referring to the Light of Christ. I've included some of its summary here:

> [The light of Christ is] divine energy, power, or influence that proceeds from God through Christ and gives life and light to all things. It is the law by which all things are governed in heaven and on earth (D&C 88:6–13). It also helps people understand gospel truths and helps to put them on that gospel path that leads to salvation (John 3:19–21; 12:46; Alma 26:15; 32:35; D&C 93:28–29, 31–32, 40, 42).
>
> The light of Christ should not be confused with the Holy Ghost. The light of Christ is not a person. It is an influence that comes from God and prepares a person to receive the Holy Ghost. It is an influence for good in the lives of all people (John 1:9; D&C 84:46–47).
>
> One manifestation of the light of Christ is conscience, which helps a person choose between right and wrong (Moro. 7:16). As people learn more about the gospel, their consciences become more sensitive (Moro. 7:12–19). People who hearken to the light of Christ are led to the gospel of Jesus Christ (D&C 84:46–48).[6]

I confess that I do not understand the full extent of the Light of Christ. How can one singularly defined *source* be responsible for so very many diverse and eternally significant aspects of our existence and path to salvation? As a scientist, I have far more questions than I do answers. And yet, without hesitation, I fully trust and believe in every implication of the Light of Christ. Between my years of studying light, both scientifically and religiously, and my associated experiences with light, I have come to realize that there is a depth and breadth to the power of light that we cannot fully understand in our temporal state. What is clear to me is that I have been blessed in countless ways when I have trusted in God's light, which has led me to discern more and more light through obedience to his commandments. I believe in all that the Light of Christ is in a way similar to an expression of faith from the renowned Christian author, C. S. Lewis: "I believe that the Sun has risen, not only because I see it, but because by it I see everything else."[7]

The Love of God

Despite the somewhat incomprehensible nature and extent of the Light of Christ, there is one further step we can take in our understanding of this eternal power. Up to this point, we have focused on the broad definition and effects of the Light of Christ without considering the specific association that it has to Christ. I love the following quotes from Elder Bruce R. McConkie because of the perspective he provides on the far-reaching significance of the Atonement of Christ:

> His atonement is the most transcendent event that ever has or ever will occur from Creation's dawn through all the ages of a never-ending eternity.
>
> It is the supreme act of goodness and grace that only a god could perform. Through it, all of the terms and conditions of the Father's eternal plan of salvation became operative.[8]

> All things center in, revolve around, are anchored to, and are built upon the atoning sacrifice of the Lord Jesus Christ. There is no language given to men or angels to proclaim these truths with the power and verity and dignity that should attend them. Let it be blazoned in burning fire through all the sidereal heavens that salvation is in Christ and comes because of his atoning sacrifice.[9]

All the capabilities and nature of the Light of Christ should be connected to our reverence for, and faith in, the Atonement of Christ. Why? Because the Light of Christ is one of the foremost manifestations of the

151

Atonement of Christ, which has far-reaching and even infinite power and influence and is not restricted by time (see 2 Nephi 9:7; Alma 34:10). In his renowned conference talk quoted above, Elder McConkie uses the word *incomprehensible* three times to point out that we are unable to understand *how* the Atonement of Christ is able to "satisf[y] the demands of justice, ransom penitent souls from the pains and penalties of sin, . . . [make] mercy available to those who believe on his holy name," and make it possible that "all . . . shall rise from the grave."[10] Yet, Jesus's Atonement does indeed do all this and more. It is my suggestion that the Light of Christ is one very crucial vehicle, or mechanism, for how the Atonement of Christ is able to reach the hearts and lives of all of God's children and to provide succor to "his people according to their infirmities" (Alma 7:12).

Further evidence of this connection between the Atonement of Christ and the Light of Christ is *the love of God*, meaning both the love of our Eternal Father and the love of our Savior, the Father of our salvation. The Atonement is the supreme act that perfectly embodies the love of God for us:

> For God [meaning the Eternal Father] so loved the world, that he gave his only begotten Son, that whosoever believeth in him should not perish, but have everlasting life. (John 3:16)

> [Christ] so loved the world that he gave his own life, that as many as would believe might become the [children] of God. Wherefore you are my [child]. (Doctrine and Covenants 34:3)

It is the love of both the Father and the Son for us that made the Atonement of Christ possible, and the Atonement is the ultimate manifestation of the love of God. Christ's Atonement makes the Light of Christ possible, effective, and powerful. It is because Christ "descended below all things" that he is able to "be in all and through all things, the light of truth" (Doctrine and Covenants 88:6). My point regarding this connection is that there is a synonymous relationship between the love of God and the Light of Christ because they are linked through the Atonement of Jesus Christ. To get a deeper sense of this connection, reflect on these scriptures and how they are interrelated:

Which light proceedeth forth from the presence of God to fill the immensity of space—The light which is in all things, which giveth life to all things, which is the law by which all things are governed, even the power of God who sitteth upon his throne, who is in the bosom of eternity, who is in the midst of all things. (Doctrine and Covenants 88:12–13)

Yea, it is *the love of God*, which sheddeth itself abroad in the hearts of the children of men; wherefore, it is the most desirable above all things. (1 Nephi 11:22; emphasis added)

Yea, they were encircled about with everlasting darkness and destruction; but behold, he has brought them into *his everlasting light*, yea, into everlasting salvation; and they are *encircled about with the matchless bounty of his love.* (Alma 26:15; emphasis added)

If you keep not my commandments, *the love of the Father* shall not continue with you, therefore *you shall walk in darkness.* (Doctrine and Covenants 95:12; emphasis added)

God is light, and in him is no darkness at all. (1 John 1:5; emphasis added)

God is love; and he that dwelleth in love dwelleth in God, and God in him. (1 John 4:16; emphasis added)

Further scriptures could be examined, but the doctrine connecting them all is the same: the Light of Christ is given to *all* of God's children, to give them direction as well as life. That light is through Christ because of his perfect love for us. Hence, God's love and the Light of Christ are essentially synonymous, though the Light of Christ can often be a more tangible embodiment of his love. The accomplished Latter-day Saint author Samuel Brown interprets the "true light" from Doctrine and Covenants 93:2 in one sense as the kenotic *agape*, which exists separate from God, connecting us to him though a metaphysical parental linkage.[11] God's love is the tree of life and the fountain of living waters (see 1 Nephi 11:25); it is planted in the hearts of all humankind, is inescapable, and fills the immensity of space; this is also true, in every one of these ways, for the Light of Christ.

Now I See

Central to the plan of salvation is our need to come to know God, truly feel and understand his love for us, and embrace the most perfect gift of that love: the Atonement of Jesus Christ. We don't need to understand the scientific extent of light in order for any of this to happen. All that is asked of us is that we stay true to what we have been given and anything else the Lord sees fit to place in our path (see Mosiah 3:19).

Is an increased understanding of gospel truths beneficial? Certainly. But it is important for all of us to be reminded that the horse is humility and faith while the cart is learning and understanding, and they should not be reversed. It is this very truth that makes the story of Jesus healing the blind man in John 9 so wonderful and compelling. So, let's return to this story.

Here was a man who had lived in a dark world from birth. Perhaps he had heard conversations on the streets of Jerusalem regarding Jesus of Nazareth; but he was without physical ability or, from what it seems, friends or family to take him to Jesus. His very own parents turned out to be more interested in retaining their social and religious status with the synagogues than in supporting their son when he was confronted by the Pharisees. When Jesus and his disciples came to this man, they had a conversation about the causes of his blindness. Perhaps the disciples even knew this man or at least had seen him around prior to that day.

After addressing the disciples' inquiry about whether it was the man's or his parents' sins that had caused his blindness, Jesus said, "As long as I am in the world, I am the light of the world" (John 9:5). As I try to imagine how this scene played out, I like to picture Jesus speaking these particular words directly to the blind man, who was now before him. How deep and multifaceted must have been the meaning of the Savior's words for this poor soul. A life of darkness and then, suddenly, there stood one before him who proclaimed himself to be the very light of the world. Jesus formed some clay, anointed the man's eyes, and instructed him to wash in the pool of Siloam. Jesus and his disciples did not actually accompany the man to the pool, but he did indeed miraculously gain his sight after washing in it.

As can well be imagined, the extraordinary healing of the blind man was astonishing to all who had seen him begging on the city streets for so many years. In fact, they were so astonished that they questioned whether it was really him or just someone who looked a lot like him; but he emphatically declared, "I am *he*" (John 9:9; emphasis added). The people asked him how he was healed, and he related to them in perfect simplicity: "A man that is called Jesus made clay, and anointed mine eyes, and said unto me, Go to the pool of Siloam, and wash: and I went and washed, and I received sight" (John 9:11).

Unsatisfied, or perhaps so thoroughly amazed, the people decided to take the man to their spiritual (and in many ways, political) leaders, the Pharisees. Again, with simplicity, the now-healed man related, "He put clay upon mine eyes, and I washed, and do see" (John 9:15). Refusing to believe what clearly was a difficult miracle to deny, the Pharisees called in his parents to try and debunk the idea that he was born blind.

Upon being summoned, the man's parents likely shook with fear before the powerful panel of Pharisees. Why? Because they knew that if they said anything to suggest support of Jesus as the Christ, they would be socially rejected or "put out of the synagogue" (John 9:22). It is fascinating that the parents clearly knew of Jesus and had chosen not to follow him, while their once-blind son seems to have only just learned Jesus's name but was ever seeking him.

The confirmation from the parents that their son was indeed born blind left the Pharisees with nothing more to disprove the miracle before them. They brought the "man that was blind" back again and counseled him to "give God the praise: we know that this man [meaning Jesus] is a sinner" (John 9:24). Then comes one of my most loved interchanges in all of scripture:

> He answered and said, Whether he be a sinner or no, I know not: one thing I know, that, whereas I was blind, now I see.
>
> Then said they to him again, What did he to thee? how opened he thine eyes?

> He answered them, I have told you already, and ye did not hear: wherefore would ye hear it again? will ye also be his disciples? (John 9:25–27)

How bold. How wonderfully courageous! This once-blind man, likely still within days of receiving sight for the first time in his mortal life, stood before one of the most powerful panels of his day and soundly rebuked them for being spiritually deaf. He could tell that they were doing all in their power to dismiss the miracle because it went against their agenda. Taken aback by his retort, they "reviled him, and said, Thou art his disciple; but we are Moses' disciples. We know that God spake unto Moses: as for this fellow, we know not from whence he is" (John 9:28–29).

Imagine the honest bewilderment this man must have felt as he stood before the religious authorities of his time, and they did nothing but refute the person who had performed an undeniable miracle. The man's response is perfect: "Why herein is a marvellous thing, that ye know not from whence he is, and yet he hath opened mine eyes. . . . If this man were not of God, he could do nothing" (John 9:30, 33).

The Pharisees had had enough. They cast him out from the synagogue, undoubtedly with the demand that he never return. What happens next is the part of this story that, to me, embodies the love of our Savior more perfectly than any other. Because his love is also his light, even the Light of Christ, this also is the story that comes to my mind as I ponder how this power works.

Consider for a moment those times in your life when you have been rejected or downtrodden by circumstances or decisions made. Perhaps you've been ridiculed for something, even something you did that was right. And yet, no one in this world could possibly understand. Certainly no one could help. It is then when Jesus, in his unrivaled love and mercy, will always be there. There is no darkness that he cannot penetrate with his light. After all, as he had said to the blind man in those still-dark streets of Jerusalem, "I am the light of the world" (John 9:5). After being cast out by the Pharisees and rejected by his parents, the once-blind man is alone . . . until:

Jesus heard that they had cast him out; and when he had found him, he said unto him, Dost thou believe on the Son of God?

He answered and said, Who is he, Lord, that I might believe on him?

And Jesus said unto him, *Thou hast* both *seen him*, and it is he that talketh with thee.

And he said, Lord, I believe. And he worshipped him. (John 9:35–38; emphasis added)

Jesus will always find us. Should you take nothing else away from this book, please remember that. Accept the reality that there are no barriers too thick, no caves too deep, no sorrow too profound for his light to penetrate. It fills the immensity of space, so why not the confines of your soul? It is a scientific fact that light is capable of transmitting through and even breaking down obstacles in its path. As mortals, we have managed to move light through the vast expanse of space and, at the other extreme, have managed to confine light inside of microscopically small wires that extend over thousands of miles. Shouldn't we more readily embrace the miracles that God can do with this marvelous spiritual radiance? After all, God *is light*. Look at the counsel given by Elder Jeffrey R. Holland regarding God's all-reaching light:

However late you think you are, however many chances you think you have missed, however many mistakes you feel you have made or talents you think you don't have, or however far from home and family and God you feel you have traveled, I testify that you have not traveled beyond the reach of divine love. It is not possible for you to sink lower than the infinite light of Christ's Atonement shines.[12]

Even the visible light that God shines for us is a manifestation of his unbounded love for his children. As was quoted back in chapter 6 from Elder Theodore M. Burton:

God's light includes the physical light we see, which makes us feel so warm and comfortable....

The light of Christ therefore includes not only spiritual light but also physical light, and is a key to understanding that form of energy which is represented by the light we see all around us.[13]

In a way, we can increase our closeness to and understanding of God through observations of all of his light. Have you ever paused a moment amidst a hectic day to admire the grandeur of sunshine as it passes through the clouds? Or have you perhaps enjoyed a rainbow, that colorful manifestation of light that has been uniquely reflected and refracted by rain? No matter where you have lived in this world, you've undoubtedly had a front-row seat to the majestic display of light that is offered during sunrise or sunset in a partly cloudy sky. All these manifestations of light are emblematic of God's love—not his love of beauty or even his love of the world, but they represent his love for you and for me. I firmly believe they are as grand and intentional a witness of his love as any angelic manifestation.

While teaching his disciples the importance of loving *everyone*, even those who use or persecute us, the Savior gave the most insightful comparison to the Father's love: "That ye may be the children of your Father which is in heaven: for he maketh his sun to rise on the evil and on the good" (Matthew 5:45). Majestic manifestations of light are painted across the skies for all of God's children to see. The warmth of his shining sun (and Son) is steadily present for all to feel. If we do not find him in the light, it will not be because he is not there—he is familiar with shining in darkness and the "darkness comprehend[ing] it not" (Doctrine and Covenants 34:2). God's love is a beacon that will never go dark, a trumpet that will ever be sounding, even the voice of the Good Shepherd that "hath called after you and is still calling after you" (Alma 5:37)—will you hearken to his voice?

An Everlasting Light

It was far more than physical sight given to the blind man that day on the streets of Jerusalem. Coming to know Christ through believing and exercising faith brings us discernment of greater and greater spiritual light. In one conceptualization, that light radiates from us, and as it brightens, so also does our comprehension of all things. Just as a spotlight reveals finer detail in a dark room, so also does our increased spiritual light enhance our perspective of the world around us. As we strive to have an eye single to the glory of God, we become like him, preparing ourselves to ultimately meet him and "see him as he is" (1 John 3:2): glorious, bright, and full of light.

While it may be difficult to imagine what that day will be like when we meet our Savior again, there is one thing you can know for certain: there will be light—and lots of it. The more familiar we are with that light, the better we will be able to abide it. After all,

> The sun shall be no more thy light by day; neither for brightness shall the moon give light unto thee: but the Lord shall be unto thee an ever-lasting light, and thy God thy glory. (Isaiah 60:19)

While we have learned a great deal about light through scientific advancement, there is so much that we still do not know. How many other ways can information be encoded into photons of light? In what ways might light be modified by other media that it passes through in the expanding universe? What other effects can light have when interacting with matter that is "more fine or pure" (Doctrine and Covenants 131:7) than what we can see? For these, and countless other unknowns, there are exciting years ahead on the path of discovery. Along every step of this path is the opportunity to embrace the central, unified, and eternal truths of our Heavenly Father's plan of salvation, which gives purpose to all that is known and unknown in the universe.

Spiritual light enables us to see truth by increasing our ability to discern the finer details of a situation or person. We feel truth in the warmth and comfort of light as it shines from the sun or accompanies the companion-ship of the Holy Ghost. As we remain faithful to the light we have received, we come to know truth so that our knowledge in that truth, illuminated by the light, is perfect (see Alma 32:34). Just as the once-blind man in John 9 came to *see* the world around him, *feel* the love and compassion of the Lord, and *know* the reality of Jesus's divinity and power, we also can see, feel, and know truth through the unmatchable power of the Light of the World. We may not know the precise equations that govern the physics of spiritual light, but we do have countless manifestations of its reality and power. As President Dieter F. Uchtdorf taught, "Just because we cannot see something with our physical eyes does not mean it doesn't exist. . . . The universe is filled with wonders profound and astonishing—things that can be comprehended only through spiritual eyes."[14]

I admit, it is exciting to think that this book might offer some readers an increase in knowledge about the physical properties of light and that new insights regarding the possible source and function of spiritual light might also be gained. It may even be possible that one of the recounted experiences or scriptural commentaries finds special meaning for a few. Yet, in my opinion and from the very depths of my soul, I hope that all these takeaways are secondary to the readers' understanding that Christ *is* the light and that without him, we are in darkness. His love is infinite, his grace everlasting, and his arms of mercy extended. May we all more fully heed his ceaseless call, embrace his outstretched arms, and bask in the warmth of his eternal light. By so doing, it will not matter what the surrounding scenes or circumstances are that bring us to our reunion before the Master. We will see him as he is, and we will be enveloped by the loving embrace of the very Light of the World:

> Then spake Jesus again unto them, saying, I am the light of the world: he that followeth me shall not walk in darkness, but shall have the light of life. (John 8:12)

Notes

1. Dieter F. Uchtdorf, "The Hope of God's Light," *Ensign*, May 2013, 70–77.
2. K. Hamrick, "2016 Doctorate Recipients from U.S. Universities," *National Science Foundation*, https://nsf.gov/statistics/2018/nsf18304/static/report/nsf18304-report .pdf.
3. For a list of some of the most prominent unsolved problems in the field of physics, see https://en.wikipedia.org/wiki/List_of_unsolved_problems_in_physics.
4. There is such beautiful and compelling scriptural language regarding the outstretched arms/hands of the Lord, including that found in 2 Nephi 1:15; Alma 5:33; 34:16; Mormon 5:11; 6:17; and Doctrine and Covenants 6:20. This gesture signifies his great, inviting love for us and has been studied in considerable

depth. See, for example, David Calabro, "'Stretch Forth Thy Hand and Prophesy': Hand Gestures in the Book of Mormon," *Journal of the Book of Mormon and Other Restoration Scripture* 21, no. 1 (2012): 46–59.

5. Light from the sun enables photosynthesis from plants, which yields oxygen for us to breathe; hence, light is quite literally the breath of life.

6. "Light, Light of Christ," Guide to the Scriptures, https://churchofjesuschrist.org/scriptures/gs/light-light-of-christ.

7. C. S. Lewis made this statement in an essay titled "Is Theology Poetry?" that was presented in 1944 at an Oxford debating society called the "Socratic Club." In 1962, "Is Theology Poetry?" was published in a collection of essays called *They Asked for a Paper*.

8. Bruce R. McConkie, "The Purifying Power of Gethsemane," *Ensign*, May 1985, 9.

9. Bruce R. McConkie, "The Three Pillars of Eternity," *BYU Speeches*, https://speeches.byu.edu/talks/bruce-r-mcconkie_three-pillars-eternity.

10. McConkie, "Purifying Power of Gethsemane," 9.

11. Samuel M. Brown, "Mormons Probably Aren't Materialists," *Dialogue: A Journal of Mormon Thought* 50, no. 3 (2017): 39–72. In particular, the following from page 60: "This *agape* is parental in its mechanics and its experience. Parents feel visceral identity with the child and can empty themselves out for the good of the child—the emptying out that the New Testament refers to as *kenosis*, especially with regard to Christ and what the Book of Mormon calls his 'condescension.' Few people love anyone as much as they love their children."

12. Jeffrey R. Holland, "The Laborers in the Vineyard," *Ensign*, May 2012, 31.

13. Theodore M. Burton, "Light and Truth," *Ensign*, May 1981, 29.

14. Dieter F. Uchtdorf, "Be Not Afraid, Only Believe," *Ensign*, November 2015, 76–79.

Index

About the Author

Aaron D. Franklin is a professor of electrical and computer engineering and chemistry at Duke University. A native of Phoenix, Arizona, he earned a bachelor's degree from Arizona State University and a doctorate from Purdue University, both in electrical engineering. Prior to becoming a professor, Franklin worked at IBM as a research scientist, studying nanotechnology. He and his wife, Lianne Walters Franklin, are the parents of three children and reside in Cary, North Carolina.